The View from the
from the
Clinic

ONE NURSE'S JOURNEY
IN ABORTION CARE

FAN BLADE PUBLISHING

8 The Green, STE B
Dover, DE 19901

ISBN: 979-8-218-02973-9 (paperback)
ISBN: 979-8-218-02972-2 (ebook)

Ordering Information:
Special discounts are available on quantity purchases by corporations, associations, and others. For details, visit http://www.theviewfromtheclinic.com.

Disclaimer:
This book is a mix of memoir and fiction. It reflects the author's present recollections of experiences over time as well as a few fictionalized stories based on actual events. All names and characteristics have been changed, some events have been compressed, and most dialogue has been recreated. Any resemblance to current events, locales or persons is entirely coincidental.

The View
from the
Clinic

ONE NURSE'S JOURNEY
IN ABORTION CARE

PATRICE D'AMATO

For L.F.D. and books never written.

"We all hunger for stories. Stories give form to our desires, feelings, and goals, molding how we view just about everything—from our own bodies to what is sacred or profane, good or bad, possible or impossible...it is from the stories we are told that we in turn unconsciously fashion our own life scripts."

—Riane Eisler, *Sacred Pleasure: Sex, Myth, and the Politics of the Body*[i]

mo·sa·ic
/mō-ˈzā-ik/

noun

1. a picture or pattern produced by arranging together small, colored pieces of hard material, such as stone, tile, or glass.
2. BIOLOGY

an individual (especially an animal) composed of cells of two genetically different types.[2]

mosaic novel

A book of short stories that share a common setting or characters and which, taken together, form a larger narrative.[3]

Table Of Contents

Part Two · 123

Part Three · 203

Introduction

THIS IS NOT THE type of writing that I would truly like to do, the kind that would make everyone feel inspired, noble, courageous, or warm and fuzzy. Or the kind that might be the subject of a TED Talk down the line. Oh, no. And yet, I feel like it might be okay and safe and right to put my fingers on the keyboard as they itch to get the story right. Let me just start by saying that I am a nurse—with part of my time spent at an abortion clinic. In almost 38 years in nursing, I've practiced in a variety of specialties and, frankly, many of them have been way more medically challenging than my 8 years at the abortion clinic where the work is fairly uncomplicated, safe, and predictable. For me, this line of work has only been really, truly interesting in that society perceives it so very differently from just about any other kind of patient care.

Far too much attention these days rests on a divisive debate that is deeply misunderstood by almost all of the good citizens on Planet Earth: pro-life and pro-choice (not to mention pro-abortion, but I'll get to that later). I can tell you that while I land on the side of choice, I am not necessarily happy about it. I can also say that, like it or not, abortion is a very, very routine and common part of everyday health care, with one in every four American women having experienced an abortion at some point in their lives. This is happily a 25 percent decline from a mere 15 years ago when almost half of all American women experienced having an abortion.[4]

Much as polite society limits its knowledge about unsavory topics like abortion, so too does it fail to grasp much about the lived experience of nurses. While I have always gotten the cocktail party variety of comments such as, "Oh, I could never be a nurse," and, "Oh, my mom/sister/aunt is a nurse; good for you!" I rarely offer any specifics on the *types* of nursing I've done—and really, not too many people are terribly interested in that anyway. We are the surprisingly silent four-million-strong workforce that attends to birth, death, and everything in between (so, you know, the heroes of health care, blah, blah, blah). I am generally not interested in grabbing my cheap five minutes of fame by revealing that I chose to work for a short while in abortion care.

But if it does come up, I am quite familiar with the universal sudden jerk to attention that's followed by either physical recoil or a salacious gleam in the eyes of those who could use this opportunity to retell some shockingly juicy tidbits to their friends later. Frankly, this is a little off-putting. And so deeply, unsatisfyingly incomplete. I fail miserably when inquisitive friends ask me to share stories about my experience at that most dreaded and taboo of places. They tuck in, genuinely curious, but I never truly feel that I have conveyed the tragedy, the comedy, the mundane, and the sometimes dead-eyed, factory-line type of work that I did. I leave them feeling highly unsatisfied by my inability to dig deeper, to give them a satisfying slice of the pie that they can digest and fold into the fabric of their personal worldviews.

Therefore, I offer you this. I am very, very tempted to run to my safe place and write a thoughtfully researched scholarly article in impeccable APA format on the topic at hand, and as a seasoned nurse educator, it is both a duty and a pleasure for me to delve into the literature at times to give you a fully informed picture of abortion care in the pages that follow. But for now, I feel certain that the most compelling gift I can give the uninitiated is a story from my soul. And yes, it is uniquely from *my* soul to yours. I have not personally experienced an elective abortion; I myself am a very boring, suburban White woman, married for over 30 years, with the requisite two and a half children and white picket fence. Okay, if you ask about my half of a child, I will tell you that I suffered a miscarriage, and the essence of that pregnancy is a story unto itself. (I will share that later.) Suffice to say that the medical term for a miscarriage is *spontaneous abortion*, and the experience is a close cousin to that of elective abortion.

I remember so clearly feeling alone in my experience, then saw firsthand how much more isolating it was for my patients. To write a book about all of this is not something I particularly wanted to do, but a tiny voice kept whispering to me that it's what's needed right now. My dearest wish is that those of you who dare to journey with me in the pages ahead will come away with a deeper sense of understanding as I make my case for normalizing the glorious messiness of human life. Just as a mosaic can come together from seemingly random bits of flotsam and jetsam washed up on the beach, my memories have coalesced to form a worldview that offers, at least for me, a measure of peace. May we dare to bring our stories out into the light as we laugh, cry, and marvel together at the universality of our experiences.

So there, I'm pretty sure I just started writing a book...

Part One

ONE

Shifting Gears

*"Today is your day! Your Mountain is waiting.
So...get on your way!"*

—Dr. Seuss, *Oh, the Places You'll Go!*

HOW DOES A MODERATELY liberal, cisgender, heterosexual, White woman with a newly minted master's degree as a nurse practitioner decide it would be a good idea to ditch her nice hospital job as a staff educator to work in that dreaded cesspool of hell, the abortion clinic? Quite honestly, I shocked even myself. Like most providers, I had referred patients or taken care of women who had had an abortion, but it was a little unsavory to think about.

I recalled our discomfort in nursing school when the subject came up in our obstetrics rotations. There was the inevitable discussion of how to figure out whether you could personally participate in terminations on the off chance that a sad case came through that day. Hospital abortions are reserved for the most difficult of cases, and they are generally rare, involving nonviable pregnancies—such as when the fetus develops without sufficient brain matter to survive—or those that pose a serious health risk to the mother. I remember thinking, as a neophyte nursing student all of 19 years of age, that I would be okay with participating in those cases, but the thought still made me sick to my stomach.

In case you are wondering, in my experience, this dilemma is not nearly as dramatic in the workplace as you might think. Except for the mandatory rotations for all medical and nursing students, everyone who works in OB has chosen their field well aware of their personal limitations, and they've made peace with what they do. Pro-choice professionals do their thing, and pro-lifers tend to work in Catholic institutions that jibe with their personal or religious views.

That said, there will always be the odd case that niggles at your soul, in which case you turn to your colleagues with *that look* and know they've got your back. Mind you, it's not often about morality; more than likely, it stems from your own personally held dark fears and traumas that rear their ugly heads: the kid who was raped by her brother who now presents with a surprise 20-week pregnancy—after all, it's hard to know that you're pregnant when you are 12 and have never had a period before—or maybe something far less dramatic but inexplicably traumatic, like the patient who looks so much like your best friend who is desperately trying to get pregnant. It's hard to uncover, sometimes, what will make you snap, but rest assured, no matter *what* area of patient care you are in, the day will come when you simply crumble and have to figure out later why the hell that one situation bothered you so much.

But I digress.

So, there I was, oh so tired of the behemoth that was (and still is) the modern hospital and its endless need to consume and mold the labors of everyone working inside it in order to maintain its own reputation for sophistication and excellence. From patients being stripped, literally, of their identities to staff learning how to fit into an incredibly complex social structure, this artificial environment was really stifling. I wanted to experience caring for people in their native habitat.

I forget how I even found out about the women's center job. No matter, my curiosity got the better of me and I decided to go in for an interview. I felt pretty badass and a tiny bit smug to be walking into a busy abortion clinic. "Oh, no, I'm not here like the rest of these desperate people crammed into the waiting room; I have an appointment with the director," was the paraphrase of what I was saying to myself as I waded through the sea of men, women, and children and was whisked past them after a few moments instead of a few *hours*.

I must pause here and tell you that my experience was primarily centered on surgical abortion, although we did do a small number of medical procedures as well. Let me explain. When a woman chooses to have an abortion, she has one of two options: she can have a surgical procedure (also known as an in-clinic abortion, or dilation and evacuation), or she can take a pill that will cause an abortion at home later. Until recently, most women (about 70 percent) have chosen the surgical option since it is quicker and can be done under anesthesia.[5] However, medical abortion procedures that can be managed via telemedicine have recently skyrocketed in popularity.[6] Not surprisingly, the trajectory and flow of patient care in medical abortion is rather different, so I will limit most of my writing in this book to those same-day surgical abortions performed in the clinic.

Therefore, let me describe to you the waiting room of an abortion clinic on a busy surgery day. After hurrying past the protesters chanting, yelling, or pleading with you to have mercy on your unborn baby, you buzz in to find yourself in a very, *very* busy reception area (think of the deli counter the day before Christmas). You get assigned a number and have to wait patiently for yours to get called. In the meantime, you settle in to survey the hordes of customers also waiting, only this is a tad more interesting because of the various reasons and ways that everyone is here. *Why on Earth would people bring their kids?* you think, rolling your eyes. And how about having eight people show up for one patient—*really, how many hands can you hold at the same time?*—taking up precious seats that could be used by those arriving for later appointments, many of them pale and overflowing with saliva from extreme morning sickness, spitting continuously into paper cups. I *will* say that I was always really happy to see those folks leave nausea-free later that day.

Quite quickly, I learned that abortion care is absolutely *not* limited to teenagers with silky ponytails or to beautiful fallen mistresses, as I had in my mind. Truly, I don't think I've ever, in all my 38 years as a nurse, seen a more diverse cross section of the human population. More often than not, the women seeking abortions were already moms to one or more children. So, back to that point about the idiotic idea of bringing kids to your abortion. Why the hell do you think they were seeking an abortion?

THEY DON'T HAVE FUCKING NANNIES, PEOPLE! As for the ones who have seven other people show up with them, I agree that it might've made just the tiniest bit of sense to minimize the number in their support groups, which some do at the behest of the clinic ahead of time. However, this is often where cultures collide, and I've come to appreciate that for many marginalized people, it feels like there is safety in numbers.

Duly rattled, I followed the busy head nurse, who was still wearing her operating room attire, to the administrator's office. Here is where I found everything that I had expected: the fierce rainbow flags and female empowerment propaganda typical of an administrator's working space. After chatting about the job responsibilities, salary, and benefits, the administrator saw the dubious look on my face. She pulled out her final selling point, one that I could tell she used a lot to persuade longtime hospital nurses who were quite determined to get out of the twenty-four-seven grind. I took the bait as she said at the end, "You know, this is a rough business, but not only do you *not* work nights, Sundays, or holidays, but you get to care for young, healthy patients, not sick and frail people."

Hmmm...how nice might *that* be for a change?

So, my friends, there you have it. Lest you think that I was a fearless crusader for the rights of women, let me be clear that while many noble and courageous people have indeed been inspired in this way, I was not and probably will never be one of them. Oh dear, no. I was tired of old people, really sick people, and the less-than-fulfilling job of chasing down staff to teach them CPR every year, sometimes on Saturday at 11:00 p.m. Plus, I had young kids at the time, and a suburban job with free parking a few miles from my house was a tiny bit enticing after hoofing it to the city year after year. It was time for a change.

This inspires me to tell you about my coworkers. I was intrigued to learn what kinds of people are called to provide abortion care. I envisioned idealistic young counselors, motherly and fiercely protective aides or nurses, and spirited young doctors out to right the world's wrongs. What I got was a mixed bag: a smattering of idealistic counselors and nurses who rarely stayed more than a year, a quirky Native American woman who was a humorous jack-of-all-trades, some unsurprisingly odd duck physicians who breezed in and out, and the hardworking backbone of the organization—smart Black women who went about their jobs unfazed by the political and ethical strife of the worried middle class. They'd seen it all before: the moralizing on both sides, political grandstanding, intimidation, threats, you name it. It wasn't and never will be anything new.

Even as slick, earnest politicians blaze through poor neighborhoods at election time and preachers shout and slam their fists saying that God will provide, the good people at the clinic just keep working. They watch with mild interest as trends come and go, knowing all the while that the work still needs to be done, year in and year out, for poor people and rich folks and everyone in between: the intimate and routine cleanup of all that is messy, shameful, and so very hidden in the human condition. Some of my greatest heroes are still plowing away at that front desk, answering every kind of question and placidly facing misplaced rage from desperate or humiliated souls lashing out at them about the unfairness of their situations.

Now let me tell you about my favorite character, by far. I will change her name and alter her story a little for privacy's sake, but I hope I can capture her essence. It perhaps comes as no surprise that it takes a unique individual to handle the cash flow surrounding this procedure. Costs vary, and due to Medicaid and other insurance restrictions, most people pay out of pocket, with median expenses reported between $475 to $895 at the time of this writing.[7] With the cashier's office right next to mine, I got to hear quite a bit from the multifaceted transactions that took place in the office of Anna Maria Giancarlo.

If you've ever been to the gritty northeastern region of the country, then surely you have met her or her immediate kin. If not, I will try to paint a picture as best I can of a prototype of my Italian American heritage—think of Marisa Tomei in *My Cousin Vinny*.

The fact that Anna Maria was a card-carrying Catholic parishioner at Our Blessed Lady of the Annunciation Church seemed not to faze her in the least with respect to her day job. She ran her operation with tight efficiency and tough love before picking up her kids at parochial school and helping the PTA-sponsored bake sales to end abortion. Her matter-of-fact demeanor with pleading fast-talkers or dejected patients who were short on funds never wavered. The really shitty thing about paying for an abortion, unfortunately, is that with every passing week that you postpone for lack of funds, the more expensive the procedure gets—as a fetus grows, the techniques need to change. Sorry, folks, for turning anyone's stomach here. When she could, Anna Maria worked harder than anyone to scare up precious dollars from the few emergency funds we received from various sources for truly desperate patients.

I once gathered up the courage to ask the slightly intimidating Anna Maria how she reconciled her job with being able to sit at Mass every Sunday and listen to relentless priestly tirades against abortion. She patiently peered at me through her tortoise-shell-framed glasses as if I were surely the world's biggest moron, shrugged her shoulders, and said that a job is a job. As with almost any employee at a women's clinic, she saw her job as work that needed to be done, with very little time to waste pondering the great ethical dilemmas of our time. It seems that the eventuality of eternal burning in hell has no place in a busy wife and mother's worry space when the car payment is due and the kids' Catholic school tuition needs to be paid.

As for me, I chose this work environment not only for the myriad reasons I mentioned earlier, but also because, truth be told, the whole thing fascinated me. I have always loved exploring the odder skeletons in life's closet. Would you like my grand-scheme view of the miracle of life? For it *is* a miracle—from the seeds that sprout and shoot up and down in both directions, reaching for the sun while simultaneously sending delicate roots into the earth, to that magical moment when a human sperm meets an egg. It is all richly, deeply miraculous. Truly though, it is the luxury of feeling safe, well fed, and rested that allows me or people like me to be able to step back to examine this miraculous phenomenon. We'll explore this later, but for now I will stick to my narrative of the very human business of everyday life and death.

The stories that follow in Part I of this book are vignettes that have stayed with me through the years. The names and details come from my own imagination as I try to conjure up composite images of the people I've served. At the risk of sounding insensitive, I honestly cannot remember a whole lot of details about the hundreds, perhaps thousands, of patients I've cared for through the years. Most of these situations are rather common and happened more than once in my experience, so I have collapsed and rearranged this cast of characters from the recesses of my memories of what seems like lifetimes ago.

Because I feel strongly that the abortion experience is never limited to what happens in the clinic, I will share with you, in Parts II and III, more fictionalized stories that are grounded in fact, told from patients' and families' points of view, and based on my own cherished memories and ideas. I offer all of this to you with great love and affection.

Welcome to my world.

TWO

Formative Years

Be careful what you say to your children.
They may agree with you.

Nathaniel Branden, *Honoring the Self*

BEFORE GOING ANY FURTHER, I must tell you about my mom, Doris, the woman who unwittingly inspired me to work with abortion patients in the first place. As a nurse herself, it was certainly a surprise when I announced my intent to place myself in this grotesque and unsavory pit of health care, especially with so many other options available.

When I told her that I had decided to work at the women's center, she was less than thrilled about my career choice.

"Patrice, you have two young children, and you live nearby. Do you really think it's worth it to risk your safety? And, you know, it will be pretty difficult to tell everyone where you work. I mean, *I'm* okay with it, but most of our friends and family... well, I don't like to unnecessarily ruffle any feathers."

And so, I reminded her of the stories she had recounted many times to me and my sisters as we came of age. She grew quiet and knew that her feisty daughter was the product of her own powerful experiences. As with many young moms in the sixties, despite her prim fondness for decorum, the seeds of feminism were germinating carefully out of sight as she cooked meals, cleaned the house, and washed endless loads of diapers. Hers was a split world, an either/or of choices that forced her to leave her professional aspirations behind in order to fulfill her equally strong desire to marry and have a family.

My mom, to the horrified worry and secret pride of her rural family, decided to leave her country roots and go to the big city for nurses' training at a large urban hospital. As the only one of their daughters not to get pregnant before marriage, her parents quietly supported what they saw as their one model child in fulfilling her dreams. Always in awe of her aunt—a career gal who became a nurse-anesthetist—my mom had big dreams of living such a sophisticated existence. Her parents packed the car and drove her to her school in the heart of an inner-city neighborhood infamous for its high crime rate, even in those days.

They needn't have worried. Unlike regular college students, these young women and the occasional man were heavily supervised and indoctrinated into a monastic lifestyle. Allow me to describe the living conditions for nursing students in the 1950s that persisted, for many, well into the '80s. I myself am a product of this lifestyle, having gone to a diploma school (at the insistence of my mother) at a time when most aspiring nurses were opting for four-year university degrees.

Like her, I lived in a dormitory connected to the hospital, an all-female residence with strict rules and even a "house mother" who manned the front desk around the clock to keep track of the students' comings and goings. In my mother's day, she couldn't even let her own mother into her dormitory, and she had to follow rules about everything from the correct way to polish her shoes to dating. If a student decided to get married, they had to leave the program and basically the profession. My mom wisely decided to marry just after she graduated but had to put her career on hold after the birth of her first child a year later. For any married woman of even modest means, there were virtually no options for things like day care, let alone the notion that a woman would actually pay someone else to care for her children unless she was of high social or professional status.

The stories that my mom shared ranged from experiences in surgery, the emergency ward, and everything in between. Like Bobbie Spencer in the popular soap opera *General Hospital* who showed up as the nurse in every single scene—whether it was dabbing the forehead of a dying patriarch or assisting with brain surgery—my mom trained intensively in every specialty. Back then, nursing students were basically free labor. They learned primarily through doing long night shifts alone, figuring things out as they went along, with only the occasional supervisor stopping by. My mom thought it was great.

She grew especially fervent when she recounted her experiences from the maternity ward. Even in the late 50s, this urban medical center was a true inner-city teaching hospital that served the usual cross mix of extremely affluent and extremely poor patients that we still see today. Middle-class folks, then and now, typically go to their nice suburban community hospitals, usually only venturing into the city for treatment of complex or unusual illnesses. For a simple country girl, this was overwhelming, exhilarating, and eye-opening.

The anecdotes that stuck with me the most were about unwanted pregnancies. Her stories about the wink of the obstetrician (which my Catholic hospital colleagues assure me still goes on today) declaring that a tubal ligation must be performed during childbirth due to "scarring" or some other absurd excuse infuriated me, especially as she suggested that I should request being sterilized in this fashion during the birth of my second child. She decried the horrible cases where babies were born in the worst of conditions, but her tale about the well-to-do White lady who had been raped really got to me. The woman was forced to carry to term, you see, because it wasn't known if her pregnancy had resulted from the rape or an ordinary sexual encounter with her husband. My mom cared for her before, during, and after the delivery. She recounted the shocked silence as the baby slid out healthy, crying lustily, his skin as smooth and luscious as a caramel macchiato. She grew sick with disgust as she told us how the anguished woman wailed, "Take it away!" at the sight, and how, upon announcing the birth, her husband promptly left her.

We would sit in horrified silence around our well-worn but still stylish chrome-edged Formica kitchen table and ponder the fate of that patient and the child whom she desperately did not want. So many questions and so much helpless rage lodged in the recesses of my teenaged soul when we would talk and talk and talk. I surprised even myself when I decided to explore this much later in my career, but as I have mentioned, I had myriad other reasons, and looking back, I only now understand the legacy that drew me back to try—on some level—to change the story if for no other reason than to honor the anguish of my mother, the distraught woman, and that beautiful unwanted child.

After particularly draining days, I too would recall stories about my nursing school days. One in particular always stood out. I remember my own maternity rotation in the inner city, and how on one occasion I was assigned to a woman in a double room with another patient. I can barely recall anything about my patient other than the embarrassing moment when I tried to teach her how to properly bottle-feed her baby and couldn't get the cap off the container. As an experienced mom of three, she kindly but firmly took the can and expertly twisted the seal and handed it back to me so that my 19-year-old, red-faced self could finish my instructions.

The patient in the other bed was a 14-year-old who had given birth the day before. As I went through my ridiculous ministrations with my own patient, I watched as the other nurse tried several times to engage the young teen to take an interest in her baby. She tried many tactics, and even tried her best to seem hip, but the kid was having none of it. Here's the gist of what I remember from the last desperate exchange I overheard.

"I just found out that you're going home tomorrow, so let's work on you giving the baby a bath, okay?"

Groans and eye rolling as the child-mom glanced up from her phone call. "Nah, I just wanna sleep. I'll do it later."

"Cynthia, we've got a lot of stuff we need to cover if you're going to learn to take care of the baby."

"C'mon, give me a break, I just *had* her yesterday!"

"I know, but you're a mom now, and you've got to learn how to do this."

Cynthia flopped over on her side away from the nurse and giggled into her cradled phone. I watched the nurse walk past me, defeated.

I realize now that it takes a very special person to do that kind of nursing. As for me, I would go on to describe that day whenever someone expressed revulsion at my choice of specialty. The thought of sending that infant home with her child-mom depressed me far more than sending that same 14-year-old home from the abortion clinic so that she could continue giggling on the phone for a bit longer. I can assure you that, for me, it is the lesser of two evils, but it is important to remember that my guesses at what the future held for her might have been as wrong as could be. Maybe the mom version of Cynthia stepped it up and grew right along with her new daughter, or maybe there was a wise and warm grandma who helped that child grow up in a loving, attentive home. And maybe the clinic version of Cynthia would have gotten pregnant again in two weeks and continued a vicious cycle of three more abortions until she finally decided to carry her fourth pregnancy to full term and become a mom again at age 17. Sadly, we nurses rarely see the happy outcomes. Our worldview is slanted by the patients who return more broken than before—endless rotations of the revolving door of poverty, abuse, and misinformation.

THREE

Suburban Landscapes

"Somewhere beyond right and wrong,
there is a garden. I will meet you there."

—Attributed to Rumi, *The Essential Rumi*, Coleman Barks

I ALWAYS WAIT UNTIL my husband has gone out for groceries before I trim our shrubs or houseplants. I have learned to take on this job myself, for when he does it, it always looks like nothing has really been touched. Even when it comes to rangy bald stems with one sad and hopeful leaf sprouting out of the tip, he says he cannot bear to deny the life that he sees peeking out. He is equally likely to leave a lone cornstalk to grow bravely in the middle of a wildflower garden, again so very reluctant to end a perfectly good life. He usually shakes his head with disbelief and sadness when he surveys my handiwork, sure that I've made a terrible mistake in my draconian pruning. He acknowledges the necessity, however, when I point out how lush and green things look several weeks after my brutish attacks.

While my husband's concerns about preserving life are confined to the garden, this leads me to thinking about Joe, a pro-life protester I came to know in the years that I worked at the clinic. Every day, without fail, Joe would stand on the sidewalk outside the women's center with his protest sign. "Every Life is Precious" was written in large handwritten block letters that graced his poster as he begged, mostly silently, with steely-eyed sadness for women to reconsider going in.

In the beginning, I eyed him warily as I got out of my car and crossed the parking lot into the employee entrance. After a few days of seeing me enter the rear door, he began to recognize me and merely nodded politely. Intrigued, I asked my coworkers about Joe; to my surprise, they grew softly indulgent in saying that he wasn't really much of a problem. I soon found out why.

As it turned out, having Joe as our devoted regular was a lucky turn of events as far as pro-life protesters go. Even in the worst of weather, Joe was on the sidewalk, a solitary figure in his God-fearing fight against the slaughter of the unborn. Dressed in his frayed flannel shirt, baseball cap, and white sneakers, he was a mild-mannered older gentleman who was most certainly a bachelor or widower with lots of time on his hands. In contrast, our other protesters—just like our patients and families—were usually a diverse group with a few exceptions, most notably an eerie and disproportionate number of White men amid the sanctimonious and often angry throng.

The third Saturday of every month, congregants of the large Catholic church down the street would assemble to sing, yell, and wave sticks with dangling baby doll limbs in an attempt intimidate and perhaps invoke the wrath of their powerful spirits.

They would chant, march, and come perilously close to violence under the watchful eye of Joe, who warily joined them but always worked hard to curb their enthusiasm as they hurled insults and sometimes spat at us sinners. For reasons unknown, Joe was especially protective of the staff. It was as if he identified with and respected our commitment to a cause, even if it was tragically off the mark in his estimation.

Over time, I came to be fond of this man as he demonstrated his unique brand of devotion. Yet he was far from angelic; patients occasionally complained about him for trying to talk to them, and even one of our young counselors was shaken one day when he sweetly and urgently trailed behind her asking, "What if your parents had decided to abort *you?*"

Ah yes, *what if?* The tantalizing question stops people in their tracks. How would I feel if I had never gotten the chance to be here in this very moment? Well, I would not be here. The what ifs are so very wistful, the imaginings of possibilities and roads not taken. I've come to realize that in their purest sense, pro-lifers are idealists in a very messy world. The sanctity of life here on Earth is a theoretical concept of the highest order, and I applaud those who serve with true humbleness and devotion in response to our wretched, stinky, and difficult world. Sadly, aside from Joe's usually quiet conviction, I rarely saw love in action, mostly just self-righteous rage.

And interestingly, as I sidestepped the endless rowdy bombasts of the pro-lifers in order to serve people in need, I always saw more than a few older White guys with hardened or contorted faces. This confused me. Was it pure and simple misogyny, or something deeper? While I cannot speak for anyone's motivation to be out on that sidewalk, I can tell you that even while avoiding eye contact, I sensed many emotions pelting me from that direction: bloodlust, fury, and outrage, for sure, but also desperation and a sense that they felt they were being personally gypped somehow. I often sensed that just under the twisted rage of their rhetoric lay a deeply rooted sense that they'd not gotten their fair share of the joy and satisfaction of procreation that was their birthright. To deny this to *anyone*, even a newly fertilized egg, was an outrage.

And then I think back to my garden. Who am I to decide what lives or dies? As I judiciously prune or rip out so many planned and unplanned miraculous life forms, I find myself wincing as I snip a vibrant green branch full of buds or feel a prick of the conscience when I yank out a handful of newly sprouted shoots. It feels important to acknowledge the sentiments of the gentle Joes, the pissed-off protesters, or even my dear, devoted husband as he grieves the brutal efficiency of weeding and pruning in order to give our chosen plants some breathing room. I cannot fault anyone for doing what they truly feel called to do. I only hope that they can someday say a prayer for me while I do the same.

As for where I stand, despite my own misgivings, let me explain. I have come to a deep realization that we are all souls housed within lovely human bodies. In female form, we are designed to create opportunities for others within our own bodies through conception. I worked in service of the legions of women who had the unlucky job of making such life-and-death decisions by virtue of their sex, and I still feel solid in my conviction that it was my job to support the beings who showed up first to inhabit their amazing human forms, long before any sprouting new life took root in their fertile bodies. It has never been and never will be easy.

FOUR

The Other End
Of The Spectrum

We all worry about the population explosion, but we don't all worry about it at the right time.

—Attributed to Art Hoppe

IN ORDER TO GIVE you the full range of the perspectives I encountered, I must pause briefly to tell you about the rare individuals who are resoundingly—and often cheerfully—pro-abortion. No, I don't mean pro-choice. While I'm guessing that around 95 percent of people living in America fall into the camps of being either pro-life (believing that abortions are wrong) or pro-choice (believing that people should be able to choose), there lies an offbeat and often undiscussed group of people who believe that abortion is the way to go. I most often got a glimpse of this point of view from foreigners, whom I'll describe momentarily. Occasionally, I would run into a Native-born American who enthusiastically endorsed abortions as a great way to thin the herd, so to speak. At best, these folks reflect the cynical and often hilarious gang who invented the Darwin Awards, which recognize outstanding individuals whose contribution to human evolution is to remove themselves from the gene pool via their own stupidity. At worst, they are scary advocates of selective breeding.

To give you a snapshot of one such believer, allow me to describe another coworker, Nurse Liz. A tall, attractive, fiftyish woman, she had worked as an operating room nurse most of her career. Her legendary cynicism will be discussed later, but for now, here is my recollection of a brief conversation that gives you the flavor of her personal worldview.

Me: "Phew! What a day! We did at least thirty-five cases today. Where in God's name do all these people come from?"

Liz: "I know. They multiply like rabbits."

Me: "It's so damn frustrating, isn't it?"

Liz (shrugs): "Not really."

Me (after a slight pause): "Well, I think it's a shame that it comes to this too easily for so many of the patients I saw today. I mean, I would be thrilled to help them find a decent kind of birth control."

Liz: "Been doing this a hell of a long time, and I can tell you, people are *not* gonna go there. Too much effort, and even though this isn't cheap, crisis control is a lot easier than planning ahead." (Excellent point. Just look at how we manage the national deficit.)

Me: "Sadly, you are right." (Sigh.) "Still, I wish I could spend more of my time preventing abortions than running around on surgery days like a headless chicken."

Liz: "Really? To tell you the truth, I wish we could do more abortions."

Me (after a significantly longer pause and a slightly open mouth): "*More*? Why?" (I am now really tired but genuinely curious.)

Liz: "You see, I am not really pro-choice; I am pro-abortion. I think we should be doing public service announcements to encourage women to abort. Honestly, everyone will be a lot better off if they get this whole baby-killing stigma out of their heads and Roto-Rooter those uteruses."

Me: "Wow."

I can honestly say that I was at a loss for words that might have softened the blow of such raging hard-heartedness. Similar to the blatantly shocking homophobic or racist statements that we, as a nation, are getting accustomed to, this left me opening and closing my mouth helplessly like a dying fish. There you have it. Another viewpoint.

After you get your head around *that*, there are other places and cultures on Planet Earth where this is the more normal perspective. In fact, as you are reading this, someone from China or Russia could be scratching their head at my absurdly confusing American viewpoint. (Indeed, I've asked a few foreign friends to weigh in so far, and they are mystified by many things, not the least of which is why someone like Joe exists to stand on the sidewalk every day in the first place.)

Americans are often accused, quite rightly, of being shockingly naive and narrow minded when it comes to understanding other cultures' belief systems. We rarely travel outside our own comfort zone—literally or figuratively—preferring our own worldview as the only valid context to understand complex issues like abortion, which, turns out, isn't nearly as loaded a topic in many places. From conversations with people from Russia to Cambodia to Spain, I have gleaned that—despite a few outliers—Americans are freaks about this. For example, in sharp contrast to our generally accepted notion that once a fetus can survive outside the womb it should be able to have a shot at independence, I recently read a fascinating account in *The Atlantic* written by an American obstetrician working in Israel who wrote of her struggle with allowing terminations right up until the due date simply because a council of religious elders deemed them appropriate, which they do in more than 97 percent of cases.[8]

As another more personal example, of the many Chinese patients I saw, one couple stands out very clearly. The Lius were a quiet, polite couple who silently submitted themselves to our surgical day processes, including counseling and being asked approximately 436 times whether they were sure about their decision. By the time they got to me, their curiosity got the better of them.

After settling in to obtain the history and a physical, I asked if they had any questions thus far. Mr. Liu leaned in a bit and looked genuinely perplexed. "Pardon me, but I must ask this since you seem very qualified. We did not expect anyone to be so professional." (Well, that's sad, but it was not the first time I'd heard that comment. Makes you wonder what kinds of experiences people have had in these situations.) "Why does everyone keep asking us about our decision?"

I answered, "Well, here in the United States, this is a very controversial issue, and we want people to be sure that they are doing what they think is best for them and their families."

Mrs. Liu spoke up. "This is so strange! In China no one asks you, and you don't really have a say one way or the other. They just make you do it and that is that."

"It does go a lot quicker, not so much fussing," her husband agreed.

Most of us might be aware of the previous one-child policy in China, and so it follows that mandatory abortions were not unheard of. And, well, heck, as of this writing, forced hysterectomies are occurring in our very own detention-center backyard, so I don't know why I still clutch my pearls in surprise. Nonetheless, things like involuntary termination and sterilization get me every time.

As a person who has devoted a lifetime to trying to ease suffering, I see personal agony as nothing but a result of people not just being coerced but also engaging in self-hatred, especially according to what their particular society deems acceptable.

FIVE

Patient For A Day

Atticus was right. One time he said you never really know a man until you stand in his shoes and walk around in them. Just standing on the Radley porch was enough.

—**Harper Lee**, *To Kill a Mockingbird*

IMAGINE, EVEN IF JUST for a few paragraphs, what would happen during your scheduled abortion—if you were to hypothetically have one. For the sake of clarity, let me be your personal escort for the day, and rest assured that, as I've recently learned, from a medical standpoint, little has changed in the last 20 years.

Just as with any surgery, you are forbidden to eat or drink after midnight if you've decided, like the vast majority of patients, to pay a little extra for anesthesia that will knock you out for your procedure. It isn't mandatory, and a few intrepid or cash-strapped patients opt for a local anesthetic only; but just as in dentistry, that little bit of numbing medicine only goes so far. I would often give plenty of pep talks to the women who were headed in to reassure them that yes, it hurts, but the abortion it-self only takes three to five minutes despite the usually *very* long day leading up to it.

Seems crazy, right? Well, there are a lot of things that have to happen to ensure that, first, you are getting safe medical care and, second, that all the myriad regulatory requirements are be-ing met. Abortion clinics, not surprisingly, are still held to a level of scrutiny that is closely monitored, and any missteps can mean a quick shutdown. I've heard of some ghastly facilities in my time and am still not sure how they weren't caught sooner.

After all the registration paperwork and a thorough counsel-ing session, we shuttle you along for a bit of blood work, which not only confirms that you are, in fact, pregnant, but more importantly that your blood type doesn't necessitate the need for a RhoGAM shot—one of the greatest miracles of modern medicine, in my humble opinion. Named after the rhesus mon-key back in the '60s, Rh disease, otherwise known as hemolytic anemia of the newborn, occurs when a person with Rh negative blood is pregnant with a fetus that has Rh positive blood, which causes deadly antibody formation in the mother that can harm her next baby—unless she gets a shot of RhoGAM.[9] It has saved literally hundreds of thousands of lives.

After waiting a seemingly interminable amount of time for all that to be done, you then head down the hall for an ultrasound to get an idea of how far along you are. Once again, there is invariably a bit of a backlog, and so you settle into your plastic chair. You've been here for several hours by now. Last stop is the history and physical to sift through your medical conditions and discuss some birth control options. You are a little cranky with me by now, and I know I would be, too, if my pregnant self had been allowed nothing but a few pathetic ice chips all day.

Finally, you get to put on an attractive peach-colored patient gown, paper booties, and a cap, only to wait to be escorted into the operating room as it gets chilly in your scant attire. It is nice to be offered a light cotton blanket, but you decline, eager to gather yourself together and get this show on the road. Once you get in the operating room and assume your dignified position in the stirrups, the nice anesthetist talks to you as you drift off—and poof! You are done! Just like in all the funny videos of people doing crazy things after getting their wisdom teeth removed, you hear later on about how you were pretty comical, blowing kisses like you had just won an Oscar and thanking all the little people who made this possible.

Wheeled into the recovery room, you are met with the usual sights and sounds, a whole roomful of patients just like you who are waking up and being assisted to the bathroom. Then you zip off to the discharge lounge, where I meet you again with some of the best ginger ale and crackers of all time. A quick review of your discharge instructions, and you are good to go. Just through the door on your left that you walked through earlier, and you find your weary support group who takes you home.

SIX

Faith And Other Follow-Ups

You have a perfect right to consign us all to hell, rector, but you must allow us the choice of how we get there.

—Angus Wilson, *The Pan Book of Horror Stories*

PARDON ME FOR BEING Captain Obvious, but the experience of abortion is highly contingent on how it is perceived and dealt with by each individual person. While the debates rage on about the long-term effects of abortion, it's very difficult to tease out any overarching truths when perusing the literature, although there has certainly been some really compelling work done recently. As much as it would be nice to find unbiased studies and analyses from impartial researchers, the storms rage on. My head is starting to ache as I dig deeper into the carefully worded scholarly articles on both sides of the divide. As someone whose primary interest is to provide people—especially patients and their families—with useful information, I find myself going down rabbit holes and reminding myself to stay true to the basic tenets of both what I've learned and what I've taught in nursing school in order to think critically about what is being said.

It is important to understand that there are some really, really bad studies out there. No wonder people are so mistrustful of the information they are fed; one minute you are advised to eliminate something from your life, and the next experts are touting the great benefits of said no-no. I was frequently barraged with questions about myths that have been perpetuated by pro-life organizations, such as that abortion causes breast cancer or that the procedure leads to permanent infertility. In fact, I still see the occasional billboard on the highway that reminds us of these urban legends based on flawed research. It is a sad and frustrating situation indeed. I spent lots of time debunking myths and encouraging women to use their own common sense when thinking about these things.

The mental health issues and spiritual crises surrounding any unplanned pregnancy might be another matter for some individuals. This is absolutely no surprise given the prominent impact of societal norms of sexuality and their effect on women across all societies and cultures since the beginning of time. That said, new research also suggests otherwise. One need look no further than the American Psychological Association's exhaustive review of the scientific literature, which concludes that the risk of mental health problems following a single elective first-trimester abortion has no greater risk to mental health than carrying a pregnancy to term.[10]

Just recently, the highly publicized Turnaway Study that followed women for five years after an abortion resoundingly confirmed this and more.[11] These researchers looked at two groups of women who went to have an abortion: those who went through with it, and those who were turned away for a variety of reasons. They asked about the women's mental and physical health, their careers, their romantic lives, their professional aspirations, and even their existing and future children—and they found overwhelmingly that the women who received an abortion reported being much happier and more financially stable than the women who ended up carrying to term. This is *not* to say that the women who were turned away and ended up having the child did not love them. They most definitely reported that they did, and their children became very precious to them because, of course, that's what happens. The research is simply telling us that the ability to make choices can lead to a better overall quality of life.

But even with these remarkable findings, it should come as no surprise that there are some women —especially those who have few sources of support—who will struggle, either within themselves or from the circumstances and people around them.[12] And I would also add that, as you will see, this can be incredibly difficult for religious women who find themselves at odds with their belief systems as an unplanned pregnancy upends everything they've ever believed and their world comes crashing down.

In my years in clinical practice, I met hundreds of women and can safely say that what I saw was in line with the Turnaway Study's findings. The vast majority of patients were incredibly resilient, working through any feelings of guilt, shame, and ambivalence much as they would in other areas of their lives. After centuries of enduring outrageous restrictions and the damning judgments of politicians and religious leaders, women are masters at quietly doing what needs to be done. I do so love that meme floating around that shows the three wise men bearing grand gifts of gold, frankincense, and myrrh while three wise women arrive ahead of schedule bringing diapers, casseroles, and sanitation supplies. Lucky indeed is the woman who is surrounded by practical, caring, knowledgeable women. But this is not always the case.

I vividly remember one of my more memorable conversations with a patient that I saw at her two-week follow-up appointment. I enjoyed this aspect of my job: I would do a quick pelvic exam, provide birth control counseling, and work with patients to figure out future plans for reproductive health care—not an easy feat given the legions of uninsured women who came through our door. It was always *much* easier to discuss contraception a few weeks after the procedure, even though we did our best to arm our patients with some kind of protection as they headed home on surgery day. Thoughts of having sex again any time soon were not usually at the forefront of most women's minds as they walked out the door after a harrowing day. Many, in fact, vowed that they would never have sex again, but, of course, just like after childbirth, that hardline view almost always softens over the course of time, especially for those who have eager sexual partners chomping at the proverbial bit.

On this particular day, I remember a patient I will call Faith. I entered the exam room to see a very tensely posed young woman perched on the edge of the table. I introduced myself and asked her how she was feeling. Faith peered intently at me and said, "*I'm* fine because I am forgiven by my Lord and Savior

Jesus Christ. *You*, however, will be going to hell for what you have done."

I paused, rather stunned and not a little fascinated, before resuming the conversation. "I am glad to know that you're recuperating well and feel good about your relationship with God," I said carefully. She continued to stare me down as I did her exam and asked about her follow-up plans for birth control and continued gynecologic care. Faith assured me that she could and would be well cared for. As I was about to leave the room, Faith decided to take one more stab at it.

"So, I feel really sorry for you. I don't know how you and your cronies do this evil thing every day. It's so horrible." She squared her jaw and glared at me through her thick glasses.

I had a packed waiting room full of patients who had already been waiting far longer than they should have to see me. I cleared my throat and said, "Yes. It sure is tough. Please feel free to pray for me and, really, for all of us." This was a phrase that I really liked, actually, and used it a lot when protesters would hurl insults as I walked into work on busy protest days. I truly feel like every single one of us could genuinely benefit from heartfelt prayers for our well-being in this life or the next. I suspect that this is not what the good parishioners from Our Lady of the Immaculate Conception have in mind when they pray to end abortion, but that's okay. I, too, think it would be wonderful indeed if we could live in a world where abortion didn't exist, and equally where sexuality and contraception were not only accepted, but honored for their contributions to our incredible human journeys of expansion and fulfillment.

I think it might be worthwhile here for me to describe a

few more colorful scenarios so that readers can begin to grasp the enormous complexity of human relationships as they relate to the job of a nurse. My experience with another patient, Deanna, went something like this:

"You are healing well. It's safe to go back to all your normal activities, but make sure you ease into them. Your normal period should return in two to six weeks. Make sure you call your regular doctor if it doesn't. Do you have any questions?" I asked.

"Yes. When would it be okay to go back into infertility treatment?"

I was stumped. "Um, you are obviously fertile since you just had an abortion."

"Yes, I know. My husband and I have been trying to get pregnant for a while now, and I don't want him to know that I got pregnant by someone else. He's sure that I am the one who is having trouble conceiving. He's really anxious for me to go forward with further treatments. He's in the military though, and I don't want our doctors on base to find out either."

Dumbfounded, I was once again reminded just how privy we are, as health-care providers, to the convoluted private lives of the patients we encounter. I honestly didn't have a clue what to say. I told her that the very best course of action would be to consult with her infertility specialist and consider marital therapy or speak to a counselor to sort out their issues, but I also understood that she was wary of doing that. As a women's health nurse practitioner, I was well aware that sometimes women live in dishonest or even dangerous situations and they have numerous reasons why they opt to do the things they do. She was impatient to get a quick answer, so I suggested she should wait at least until after her first regular period, start taking prenatal vitamins, and left it at that.

This was not an isolated case of a woman asking how quickly she could try to have a baby after her abortion. Each woman has her own reasons, and there is simply not enough time in a packed schedule to allow for detailed exploration. I was usually scheduled to see 14 patients an hour with the knowledge that we generally only had a 40 to 50 percent show rate for patients returning for a follow-up visit. Some days, though, everyone was motivated to keep their appointments. Even on a good day I was usually running well behind schedule, with little more than a few minutes with each patient.

My most impactful follow-ups were with young girls who were experiencing their very first gynecologic exam. Because these kids almost always had general anesthesia for surgery, they had no memory of being placed in classic lithotomy position, laying flat with their legs spread, let alone having been examined by a clinician. They would have to experience this as part of postoperative care and coming to me was almost always a shock. I often thought about how we could best serve really young girls (we've had some as young as 11) with a balance of kindness and honesty.

Situations ranged from youngsters who were raped to those who were eager to act like the grown-ups they saw on TV. My pediatric nursing experience was limited to the six- or eight-week rotations I had had as a nursing student in the hospital years before, and I struggled with this. Honestly, with little ones under 13, I would generally forgo the pelvic exam and carefully document their reported history I would get from them and their parent or guardian. I did have a few cases that went to child protective services, but thankfully my administrator had lots of skill and experience in this area, so I was usually able to concentrate on the physical aspects of their care.

I actually really liked coaching older teenagers or women who had never previously had an exam through the process. It is a crucially important job that, unfortunately, many providers do not take seriously. So many women describe their first gynecologic exam as a nightmare of carelessness and insensitivity. No wonder they find themselves pregnant rather than relive or anticipate a painful experience of having to go to the doctor for contraception.

I remember one young woman, whom you'll get to meet later, who acidly remarked that women are held hostage by doctors so they can get paid to prescribe them birth control while also slut shaming them in the process. I knew what she was talking about. I have heard more than one hideous remark from impatient doctors when I was assisting with a patient in stirrups. It horrifies me to this day to remember, and I feel waves of remorse that, back in the '80s, I wasn't an assertive enough 22-year-old to stand up to those misogynists. The memory of standing silently beside patients still haunts me sometimes. If you have never heard someone on a cold metal exam table being told, "Stop flinching, it didn't hurt when you were having sex," I hope you can find it in your heart to feel compassion and thank your lucky stars that this has never happened to you.

I also learned so very much, in these brief encounters, about the fear and distortions that women sometimes develop from a a wide variety of experiences. Memories bubble up to the surface of my mind as I recall some of these situations. I remember the highly intelligent and feisty lawyer who was planning to sue her obstetrician for disfiguring her vaginal opening after she had a baby. She kept apologizing for the hideous deformity I would no doubt encounter when she opened her legs for the exam. I was not surprised to find a perfectly ordinary vaginal opening. When I reassured her that she looked completely normal, she grew quite defensive, then started to cry. It seemed that she was convinced that her boyfriend had left her because she had such mangled anatomy that he couldn't bear to touch her. As someone who had looked at literally hundreds of women's private parts, I assured her that I saw no reason to sue anyone. So very sad are the harsh and often distorted ways in which we feel judged in our bodies, either by a partner or by ourselves.

Another poignant moment was when I had to spend a few extra moments with a beautiful, young Lithuanian woman who was so traumatized that I could barely examine her. She kept screaming how ugly she was down there and clamped herself into a fetal position again and again. I tried to calm her down and even described the vulva as a beautiful flower, like an iris, but to no avail. Again, I can only imagine the harrowing experience that led to her terror.

This is the everyday reality of most gynecologists. I saluted them when I said goodbye to that chapter in my professional life, and I continue to salute them today, especially those who strive to engender compassion and empowerment in every patient encounter. To be completely honest, to me it was often messy—and dare I say smelly—work. The medical assistants would often roll their eyes in disbelief when I walked out of certain exam rooms and told me time and again that they didn't know how I did it as they ran in spraying the air freshener. I smile to think of a midwife friend who once said she could handle any vaginal secretions but would readily faint at the sight of a spider. It is truly a testament to our uniqueness how we are all equipped with widely divergent talents in order to bring out our best selves in service to the vast web of life.

SEVEN

Peach Gowns, Paper Booties, And Politics

"Courage is found in unlikely places."

—Gildor in *The Fellowship of the Ring* by J.R.R. Tolkien

ONE DAY AS I rounded the corner into the back hallway jammed with preoperative patients lined up in their peach-colored gowns and paper caps, I glanced toward the administrator's office at the far end of the hall. Having the formal administration office in such close proximity to our patient-care areas could be problematic at times, but the clinic was designed for efficiency. In truth, I kind of liked having Marilyn (our all-knowing administrator) near the action, although that could not be said of the various vendors or guests who occasionally had meetings with her. It sometimes got a little disorderly out in the hallway, and although patients complained mightily about being lined up like lemmings together, sometimes a sense of camaraderie developed, with women swapping stories or bolstering each other's courage as they waited their turn.

On this day, I noticed that a small group of well-dressed people had gathered in Marilyn's office. They sat chatting earnestly, and before I went down to introduce myself, I sensed who they were. At that moment, as a nearly burned-out administrator in an overwhelmingly busy clinic, Marilyn was in her element. Visits from the good folks at NARAL (the National Abortion Rights Action League) always bolstered her morale and reminded her of why she remained in the trenches. The group consisted of a carefully chosen representation of members: a political lobbyist, a lawyer, and of course several very influential donors—professionals outside of the medical world. As I sit here today, it is so easy to grasp the nonclinical world's view of abortion as one of the foremost social and political hot button issues of our time. I'd challenge you to find a person anywhere who lacks awareness or personal opinions about this topic. Morality, philosophy, social justice, religion, and law all coalesce around this intensely personal and collective phenomenon that resides exclusively in women's bodies and often affects the men whose bodies entered them. In this clamoring din, it is a challenge to also conjure up the very real, very clinical world that abortion exists in.

They were at the clinic for a tour that day, and Marilyn was eager to show them our work. However, she had had her doubts about their insistence on coming on a surgical day; usually the groups were much more comfortable arranging a time to meet that did not coincide with the hectic pandemonium, partly out of respect for everyone's time and partly out of a profound sense of dread. They talked at length about their work in the battle to keep abortion safe and legal but stretched out the discussion so as to limit the amount of time they were required to be among the swarm of actual patients. I was familiar with this. At the time, I was a part-time lecturer at a nearby school of nursing and had become well acquainted with the sometimes grueling job of teaching second-degree students in their final semester of undergraduate nursing before they moved on to their impassioned callings as midwives or women's health nurse practitioners.

Straight out of women's studies at Sarah Lawrence, or Harvard, or Barnard, these fervent, theory-loving young adults questioned everything that did not fit into their deeply fulfilling woman-centric worldview, even if they had not yet gone out into the field. More than once did I endure the withering gaze of a condescending student who, with all the wisdom conferred to her in her 26 years on this Earth, scathingly and loftily lectured me on my rockabilly denseness about the way the world can and should operate. It was exhausting.

But I also totally got the appeal of immersing oneself in the cleaner world of nonclinical work, as many of them ultimately aspired to do. In my 38 years as a nurse, I invariably ended a stint of clinical practice drained and frustrated by the long hours and relentless patient interactions and moved into a different position. More often than not I found myself gravitating toward administrative or educational arenas that meant nicer hours and tidy tasks like writing organizational policies or developing essay questions. I remember the reluctance to leave my office to face the often rough humor or hostility of busy staff members who saw me as the lab-coated enemy there to impose another unnecessary layer of bureaucratic protocol on their already overwhelming workloads. Many days it took an awful lot to steel myself to go out and interact with clinical staff who saw me as an out-of-touch prissy bitch who had no clue what a real nurse does.

After I left my patients, I saw the group stand and begin to inch their way cautiously out of the office. Like my wary house cats whenever company arrived, they trotted in single file, eyes respectfully downcast, pressed against the wall until they reached the relative safety of the lobby. Meanwhile, the patients—bored to death after hours of waiting—gawked curiously at them as the anomalies they were in this sea of paper booties and backless gowns. Some even called out to the "fancy ass people," garnering snickers from other patients, not fully aware that if it weren't for these liberal elites, perhaps they'd be stuck having a baby they didn't want.

I was simultaneously chuckling at the sight and feeling very sorry for these incredibly intelligent and ferocious people as they awkwardly waded through the very throngs of staff and patients they were fighting for. It's true that their world *was* so very far removed from this pathetic and chaotic scene of human scruffiness. And yet, without them and their unflinching toughness in society, the ability to have an abortion—as yucky as it was—could not exist. For me, the scene crystallized the sometimes strange triad of tensions that exemplified the often strained role relations in my career and personal life as a patient. At some point or another, I have played each role: the idealistic champion, the hard-bitten clinician, and even the ashamed patient masquerading as a tough girl. That these individuals are so often in opposition when they meet is truly a pity. The truth is the world desperately needs all of us.

EIGHT

Abortion Through The Ages

"Si non caste tamen caute."
(If not chastely, at least with care.)

—Popular adage used in the Middle Ages, from Wolfgang P. Müller, *The Criminalization of Abortion in the West*

TRUTH BE TOLD, I am a big history nerd, and I love nothing more than to be swept to a different time and place when thinking about how we got to where we are today. I had forgotten about the fascinating history of abortion and how very differently our not-so-distant ancestors approached this. It is quite ironic that in as little as five generations back, abortion was a highly visible and accepted aspect of American society. Check out this fascinating and quick read from the History Channel, "The Criminalization of Abortion Began as a Business Tactic," if you want your jaw to drop,[13] but I will also give you a short summary below.

Have you ever seen those funny old-fashioned newspaper or magazine ads from way back touting elixirs that would cure anything from ringworm to melancholia? Right there, among them, are ads for abortion pills or even surgical abortion services offered by unlicensed professionals, often women who earned their credentials through apprenticeship or folk medicine. Back in the day, people strongly believed that the body needed to keep things freely flowing in order to maintain a good balance. Missed periods were viewed in terms of lacking menstruation rather than the possible presence of a fetus, which in the early stages was considered nothing more than an obstruction, a clog in the system. Magic cure-all tonics and pills promising to rid the body of anything that might impede normal bodily functions were seen in much the same light as constipation or kidney stones. Pregnancy and childbirth were risky business, and doctors routinely encouraged their female patients to take quick action to bring on a late period, which usually involved taking an emmenagogue, a type of herbal preparation that brings on menstrual flow even when it is not due. Emmenagogues, it should be noted, are related to abortifacients, but not defined solely as such. An abortifacient is a substance that is known to induce miscarriage, such as specific herbal preparations or Mifepristone (also known as RU-486).[14] In other words, you don't have to be known to be pregnant to try using an emmenagogue. Even today, you can buy herbal medicines and teas over the counter at the drugstore to promote "healthy cycles" with clearly worded warnings not to take them during pregnancy. Along with the above-mentioned herbs, there are dozens of others, like pennyroyal or yarrow, that are known abortifacients that can induce a medical abortion, otherwise known as a miscarriage.[15] I am not entirely sure of their effectiveness for ending a possible pregnancy, but from the number of products I see when I peruse the health food aisle at my local pharmacy, I can tell you that people are obviously using them for something!

Note the careful wording on the ads below, especially the ones for "married ladies," whose personal health might necessitate the services of Madame Restell (1812–1878), the famous female abortionist in New York City who enjoyed a highly successful 40-year career with a legacy of being seen simultaneously as a hero to desperate women and "the Wickedest Woman in New York" to many others.[16]

As was typical of almost all doctors at that time, Restell was a self-proclaimed physician who made a comfortable living as a highly visible women's health provider whose tactics were seen as somewhat murky insomuch as they hinted at the rights of women to dabble in the dangerous territory of family planning. As described below:

> New York State law regarding abortion reflected contemporary folk wisdom, which held that a fetus wasn't technically alive until "quickening"—the moment when the mother felt it first move inside the womb, usually around the fourth month. An abortion before quickening was legal, but an abortion after quickening was considered to be second-degree manslaughter.[17]

As pictured below, Madame Restell's first notice ran in the *New York Sun* on March 18, 1839, alongside many other abortion-related advertisements, and read, in part:

TO MARRIED WOMEN—Is it not but too well known that the families of the married often increase beyond what the happiness of those who give them birth would dictate?... Is it moral for parents to increase their families, regardless of consequences to themselves, or the well-being of their offspring, when a simple, easy, healthy, and certain remedy is within our control? The advertiser, feeling the importance of this subject, and estimating the vast benefit resulting to thousands by the adoption of means prescribed by her, has opened an office, where married females can obtain the desired information.[18]

Image courtesy of Library Company of Philadelphia

As millions of people today search for folk remedies as replacements for mainstream medical care, I am not surprised to find a wealth of online information about managing fertility through alternative and complementary therapies. If you, dear reader, are anything like me and could see the appeal of seeking a "natural" way to end a pregnancy, you might be itching to do an online search for how to abort without the intervention of a traditional health-care provider. I am with you on this; I too despise the experience of going to the doctor, especially when it involves such a personal matter. The idea of remaining in the privacy of your own home using ancient and, dare I say, sacred feminine wisdom in a deeply meaningful way is very, very attractive.

That said, although it is important to remember and respect time-honored practices that allow women to explore alternatives to mainstream medical care, it is my duty to present the potential problems that are often encountered, especially when people are not thoroughly knowledgeable about the risks. It can become exceptionally risky when people dabble in a variety of modalities all in the name of self-care. In my experience, even in the most controlled clinical settings, things can and do go terribly wrong, and when you mix and match treatments from various types of health-care providers, it's really difficult and downright dangerous to tease out just what is happening.

Perhaps now is the perfect time to walk you through a nonsurgical abortion from a very personal perspective. You may recall that this is basically a miscarriage; it's generally the same physiologic experience regardless, whether you take some pills to induce bleeding or not. I am here to tell you that it hurts like *hell*, it is not without its risks, and it can take a rather long time.

During the early years of my marriage, my sister died very suddenly. About six weeks later, amid all the chaos and deep grief, I was stunned to learn that I was pregnant with my second child. I remember a not-so-distant relative raising her eyebrows while commenting that this seemed like an unlikely time to have even been *thinking* about sexual congress, and I chose to counter with a brief explanation that, for me, I could think of no more important time to hold someone I love as close as I possibly could and that tears and physical closeness are a beautiful and important way to grieve together. (I could have simply told her to mind her own business, but as you have already learned, in my younger days, I was not usually given to putting people in their place, no matter how shockingly well deserved.)

About nine weeks into the pregnancy, just after we announced the happy news to friends and family, I began to bleed. I was rushed home from work by a concerned colleague and went straight to bed as directed, but the bleeding continued. By the next day, it grew heavier and the cramping became severe. I was doubled over in pain on the bathroom floor trying not to cause our then-two-year-old daughter to panic, leaving her and my husband to carry on with their normal routines while I labored alone. For it *is* labor, make no mistake. After what seemed like hours, I finally got myself to the toilet and pushed. In time, a hard knob about the size of a peach pit landed with a splash, and I knew, good nurse that I am, that I must fish it out and bring it to the doctor with me. The pregnancy was over. I cried uncontrollably as I sat clutching my Ziploc baggie surrounded by happy pregnant bellies in the obstetrician's waiting room.

How, you might ask, did I know to bring the fetal tissue with me? As with any type of abortion, spontaneous or otherwise, it's helpful to analyze the expelled products of conception to be sure that there is nothing left behind. Even the tiniest piece of tissue can signal the uterus to continue bleeding, and this is a common reason for postpartum hemorrhage. Although it's rare, a woman can have an incomplete spontaneous or medically induced abortion and then must undergo surgical dilation and evacuation just as if they'd had a surgical abortion in the first place so they don't bleed to death. All this is to say that while it might seem a whole lot better than having surgery, medical abortion sucks too.

Imagine yourself doing all of this in a different time and place. Think Victorian America, no air conditioning, sweating bullets in your high-necked nightie crouched over a chamber pot, and forget getting anything nearly as effective as ibuprofen for cramps, thank you very much. Lest we wax poetic about the beauty of simpler times, I now give you a whole new context for the scenes in old movies when a maid comes in curtsying to apologize that the lady of the house cannot partake in the evening's festivities due to "female troubles."

My fantasies about the good ole days are always shattered by a solid reminder of the blessing of modern conveniences that now feel essential. Nevertheless, if you had lived in a society with widespread acceptance that you had done nothing shameful or immoral since you'd never felt a fetus kick, it might've been easier to deal with the physical pain because no one would have thought for a minute that you didn't have the right to stay charmingly balanced and free flowing if that was what you wanted. That's until the illustrious American Medical Association came on to the scene.

Now, you might've guessed, as did I, that the Church would've been the instigator, but no. Fascinatingly, the Catholic Church had a radically different stance on the matter than it does today. Hold on to your hats for what I am about to tell you. The holy Catholic Church did *not* espouse the belief that life begins at conception. I repeat: *Catholics did not believe that life begins at conception.* Until a little over 150 years ago, religious authorities actually supported the idea that the soul was not present in a fetus until about 40 days after conception for males and 80 days for females.[19] How on Earth did they come up with those exact numbers, you might ask incredulously? Although it wasn't an official church doctrine, clergy adopted this stance based on the venerable wisdom of St. Augustine, whose fifth-century inter-pretation of Aristotle explained that the soul enters the body only after it is fully formed at the above-mentioned ages of ges-tation. I am a little mystified why males get a 40-day jump on females in that regard but not entirely surprised at the edict, giv-en that male babies, to this day, are often favored over females. I am also forever impressed with religious leaders' self-assured arrogance that allows them the authority to proclaim the laws of God with absolute and irrefutable certainty, even more so if we are to look at the history of how religious dogma changes over time. To be sure, the world *feels* like a much more secure place if you have a religious tenet that seems timeless and secure, like a sturdy oak in the middle of the never-ending tornado of life. To the deeply devout, becoming untethered would be an unbear-able proposition.

So, what exactly *did* drive the about-face in popular and po-litical terms? During the early 19th century, folk practitioners and homegrown healers (ahem, uneducated *women*) were being slowly replaced as medical schools gave rise to a class of professionally trained doctors. Emphasis on rigorous scientific inquiry, while much needed, bestowed the gifts of skepticism and elitism as the male-dominated worldview of health and illness began to evolve. Suspicion and resentment surrounding witchy midwives and self-proclaimed doctors like the showboating Madame Restell grew quickly, and when the American Medical Association (AMA) formed in 1857, one of its very first objectives was to criminalize abortion.[20]

Let's take a collective deep breath and pause a moment before I go on. As a nurse, I am forever grateful to my physician colleagues for the breadth of skill and knowledge that was borne of this explosive movement into modern-day medicine. So many miraculous discoveries have been made, and while so very many of us are deeply dissatisfied with the lack of humanity in contemporary medical care, I must point out that a large majority of us would not be here enjoying the long lives we're able to live today were it not for the astonishing gifts that came along with the subjugation of eons of deeply held wisdom from the natural world.

That being said—and feel free to get mad again—my story continues. It was quite a job, but the AMA worked tirelessly to convince politicians that pregnancy and childbirth—along with all other aspects of health and illness—needed to be firmly placed in the hands of doctors. Intense lobbying stirred up public alarm about falling birth rates among middle- and upper-class White women.[21] The fledgling doctors' association was successfully able to instill fear that decent, married women who had abortions were stepping way out of line by using contraception and abortion to thwart God's plans. In 1873, the Comstock Laws banned the sharing of any and all information about birth control, and anti-abortion laws quickly fell into place.[22]

These bans were successfully upheld for the next 100 years, at least on paper. Of course, women continued to get abortions, legal or otherwise. It's estimated that, in the United States, as many as 1.2 million illegal abortions were performed per year in the 1950s and 1960s.[23] Not surprisingly, thousands died or suffered serious medical problems as a result. This was the era that pro-choice advocates will grimly tell you about if you can stomach the stories about coat hangers and back-alley abortionists. Thousands of women were treated by hospital emergency staffs each year after enduring desperate and often unsafe attempts at terminating unwanted pregnancies.

As seen in plenty of old movies, women of means could go to their private doctors for less dangerous, albeit still illegal, abortions. This was effectively the only moderately safe option for the first part of the 20th century. I say "moderately safe" here because doctors were only as good as their underground reputations for these things. They certainly weren't getting board certified or sharing best practices via professional journals. Historians on the other end of the abortion debate might well tell you, truthfully, that the rate of reported abortions fell nicely back in the good old days when people stayed married and accepted whatever came through thick and thin. I must point out that this number is skewed tremendously, as it would make perfect sense that reporting abortions sharply dropped into nonexistence due to the fact that doctors and hospital administrators certainly weren't going to disclose anything that might affect their newly minted licensure and accreditations.

Despite the huge the gains in general medical knowledge and surgical care that developed in the 100 years after the Comstock Laws were enacted, basically nothing changed for women seeking an abortion. And then came 1973, the infamous year of *Roe v. Wade*, when the feds struck down states' laws banning abortion.[24] As most of us know, it's been a rocky road since then, full of ups and downs, and it certainly ain't over yet, at least not in the good ole U-S-of-A. It's interesting to note that boisterous controversy continues all over the world. Recent news headlines from Poland and Argentina aside, I was completely bowled over when *Ireland*, for God's sake, recently and resoundingly overturned their anti-abortion laws in 2018 by a very comfortable margin. Don't even get me started on my shock at what's happening in South America, where several countries have recently decriminalized abortion.[25] The work it takes is dogged and unrelenting, but just as with religious doctrine, ideas of moral responsibility can and do change over time.[26]

Well, there you have my carefully researched and somewhat scholarly foray into the recent history of abortion. My takeaways? Moral tenets are products of their times. Maybe the religious right have finally hit upon Truth, but it's good to know that what's seen as true today is a direct byproduct of modern medicine, not religious doctrine. It's fascinating to realize that what we take as gospel truths that should withstand the test of time are not nearly as entrenched as we may think.

As for me, I firmly stand by the notion that each person who really cares about this must dig deep within themselves to find their Truth and find a way to be able to sleep at night. So, yes, this means that the war will rage on as impassioned people take their sides until such time comes when something changes. It all serves a purpose that I suspect is far bigger than women's rights or baby killing. The themes of right-to-choose and right-to-life are huge, all encompassing, and a mere manifestation of a world grappling with its age-old issues of self-determination versus responsibility to others.

There is *so* much more that can be said here, but I must stay true to my original intention; you didn't come here for a political or public health treatise. Our shared goal here is to give you a bird's-eye view of the world of abortion that I carry with me more than 20 years after my departure from service at the women's clinic. In the pages that follow, allow yourself to feel the stories that have shaped my unique world view. They are as alive in me now as they were then—like dear old friends that have stood the tests of time and circumstance. Even though times change, the intimate experiences I was part of typify so much of what is still happening in the lives of women all around us.

NINE

Walking
The Tightrope

"Life is a ticket to the greatest show on earth."

—Martin H. Fischer, *Fischerisms*

EVERY ONCE IN A while, the circus came to town. Unlike other occurrences—such as blizzards and holidays—which brought predictable surges of patients six to nine weeks after the event, it took me a while to discern why we would see a more unusual clientele whenever the circus was in town.

I am forever reminded of the connectivity of the outer world to the endless stream of patients coming to seek health care at any given point in time, particularly when it comes to sexual congress. Health-care personnel are, after all, not so different than other office workers who often forget that their artificially climate-controlled environment flows directly from the stream of circumstances happening in the larger outer world.

Nomadic groups like circus people needed care too and often clustered their appointments at the same time.

It was after a few cases that I began to piece together that something was up. I'd enter a room to find a stark-naked woman, legs splayed wide open, calmly waiting with the expectation that we'd skip the chitchat and get down to business. Rattled, I would tiptoe around the end of the table and gently pull the paper drape up to her shoulders while introducing myself. Pleasantly cooperative, often with a heavy Eastern European accent, these athletic young women were very businesslike and easy to work with. I came to understand that, unlike American medical culture, care in other parts of the world is often starkly efficient with very little room for privacy and/or hurt feelings.

Like hundreds of other women who work in the entertainment industry, these patients frequently sported interesting pubic hair patterns in various stages of regrowth after extensive waxing and shaving. Multiple extremes existed, with some smooth and hairless as a baby's bottom and others with dark, curly crops knotted with scarring from ingrown hairs and abscesses due to years of agonizing hair removal. More often than was ever necessary, I heard confessions from women who apologized vigorously for being unshaven, with some talking about what a relief it was not to have to pluck, primp, and posture for a week or two. Their glue-residued eyelids and sore groins got a much-needed respite from the false eyelashes and sequined thongs that lay unused in their dressing rooms while they let their bodies heal.

The tricky part of caring for these hardworking women was that they were usually just passing through, with no real home base in which to receive consistent care. This was actually how I finally figured out what was going on.

"So, you're healing well, but I'm a little concerned about the bleeding, which should be lightening up by now. Do you have a regular gynecologist that you see for checkups?" I would ask.

The answer would be the same. "No." Just that, with no explanation. I never did figure out if this was due to a language barrier or a cultural one. In that moment, I would lean into the pause and try to imagine myself as a young acrobatic trapeze artist swinging from the very pinnacle of the big top or smiling and waving to the crowd as I glided across the tightrope shifting my toes deftly in my satin slippers. Maybe I started my circus arts training at the age of six in Belarus and joined the circus at fifteen, traveling the world as I plied my craft between the endless setting up and breaking down of tents and trailers as the show went on and on, from town to town.

There's an excellent chance that my lifestyle was as unfathomable to these women as theirs was to me. I actually tried my hand at circus arts once after much encouragement from my talented niece who took me to an aerial silks class. Again and again, I slid hopelessly down the silky ropes as my fingers tried desperately to tighten enough to allow my limited upper body strength to hoist me into a thrilling pose. The instructor, sporting a rainbow-striped Mohawk with matching colorful armpit hair, finally conceded in defeat and helped me position my body on a trapeze that gave me, for two exhilarating minutes of my life, the indescribable feeling of floating in midair. I comforted my bruised ego by imagining these incredibly lithe young beings cramming information-laden index cards into their backpacks as they headed to a nearby testing center, nervously glancing at them one last time as they sat down to a grueling state board of nursing examination.

And so, we peered at one another trying to bridge a gap that was at least as wide apart as the platforms in Cirque du Soleil. I would ask about their upcoming tour schedule and give them the telephone number of the closest Planned Parenthood. Far more often than not, they would raise their eyebrows in surprise at this information, which was quite new to them. I surmised that there was a severe shortage of older women in their world who could dispense much-needed advice and support. A show for all ages is, at its core, about dazzling the crowds with youth and beauty.

TEN

Brianna, Blaze, And Brandi

"I'm too wacky for most weirdos. Who am I to judge?"

—Tori Amos, *Entertainment Weekly*, July 1996

I BRING YOU NOW to the stories about the women who mystified me in their unique ability to approach the world with a viewpoint so far from my own that I cannot possibly do justice to where they were coming from in writing their stories.

Brianna

As a person who is terribly earnest in her work and beliefs, I was in a kind of foul mood after I took care of Brianna. She fulfilled every appearance of someone who would likely be Kim Kardashian's BFF. Not gonna lie, it was rough for me to withhold judgment as she sashayed in, then plunked down her Coach handbag, expensive bracelets jangling cheerfully from her slender wrists. I introduced myself and the following dialogue ensued.

"Oh, hey, nice to meet you." Her eyes flicked impatiently around the office before landing on my unmanicured nails.

"I just need to go over some of your medical history and take a listen to your heart and lungs. Is that okay with you?"

"Yeah, whatever. Um, I have a question for you." Brianna leaned forward earnestly. She began using that singsong uptalk ending in continuous question marks that's still so popular with many teenagers and young women these days. It drove me nuts. "So, like, I'm getting married next month? And, like, will I be back to my normal size? I honestly wouldn't care if I got pregnant right away, but, like, I really, *really* wanna look good in my dress. It would totally suck if it didn't look awesome, right?"

"Well, you're only eight weeks and two days pregnant right now, so I don't see why that should be a problem. I would start prenatal vitamins and use some sort of birth control for at least two cycles before you…"

"Oh cool! Super awesome! So, um, like, do I need to sign something?" Clearly this interview was over.

I sighed as I handed her the paperwork and thought about all of the brave human beings who fought and continued to fight for her rights. I was also reminded that the decision to abort is not always heart-wrenching, and my righteous anger and judgment flared up. How could some women take this so lightly, like an errand to tick off between getting your nails done and hitting the tanning beds before your big trip to Cabo? Would it kill *you* to keep this pregnancy, this natural spark of life that would like to inhabit your being? You had said yourself that you're planning on getting pregnant anyway; what's a little tummy in the grand scheme of things?

All these years later, I can hold on to this juicy outrage as well as the best of them to justify my motives for choosing to do the work that I did. I like to view myself as a fierce, compassionate woman working to make the world a better place, but doing so is only part of my illusion about who I'd like to *think* I am. I smile wryly as I conjure up an image of the relentless pro-life OB-GYN doctor who pounds the pavement every friggin' Saturday on her days off to fight tirelessly for the rights of the unborn (check out this fascinating female anti-abortion doctor in the PBS *Frontline* documentary *The Abortion Divide*). With shattering clarity, I realize that we are not so different, she and I. The humbling truth is that we all gravitate, ego in hand, to what we're attracted to in the smorgasbord of life, be it social justice, deep desperation to perpetuate human life, or Gucci handbags.

Blaze

Let's start at the end of this story and work our way backward. Again, I am not exaggerating when I tell you that this is something that has happened more than once in my career. It's one of those things that leaves nurses—the sensible, practical, plan-ahead kind of people we have learned to be—simultaneously giggling and scratching our heads.

So, might you find it a bit odd if you go into a room to clean up after a patient and find someone's panties left behind? (Tiny pun intended.) You might imagine a nurse or medical assistant commenting to one another on the leopard-print thong strewn amid the paper gown and exam table cover that they are getting ready to dispose of. A small chuckle and the inevitable banter about how this happens would not be unlikely, especially when everyone's a little punchy after a long day. How and why does someone forget to put their panties back on before leaving? Do we really want to envision this as they run out on a windy day to catch the bus? Or maybe they carry around a spare pair? The possibilities never fail to entertain us lowly health-care folks on a busy day.

Blaze was a little different in that she amazed us by failing to wear panties in the first place. A tiny wisp of a girl with long, tousled hair and Birkenstocks, the scent of patchouli wafted behind her as she was taken from pre-op testing to surgery to the recovery room and finally the discharge lounge. She seemed a little dazed by all the medical mumbo jumbo, but she bore up amazingly well given the circumstances. As was often the case, I was the discharge nurse whose job was to administer snacks and both verbal and written discharge instructions, the latter of which I often found in the trash as I cleaned up at the end of a day. Rarely did this make me a happy camper, especially later when I could expect an urgent 3:00 a.m. phone call to our 24-hour emergency hotline that would wake me out of a sound sleep to ask if it was okay to take Tylenol for cramps.

Anyway, the lounge had small changing rooms where we placed patients' belongings so they could gather their things and get dressed. When Blaze was ready to be discharged, she floated into the changing room and was there for a few moments before popping her head out from behind the curtain, looking confused.

"Everything okay?" I asked as I saw her looking in my

direction.

"Uh, well, I don't know how to wear this pad thingy." She held up one of those very ungainly maternity pads that are standard issue in most hospital settings. You may know the kind: thick, long, with no adhesive, just long paper cloth tails. (I recently had a fun stroll down memory lane explaining these to a 29-year-old coworker who had no idea that they were designed to be worn by securing the tails through metal or plastic clips on the elastic sanitary belts of times gone by. She had to Google images of said sanitary belts because she didn't believe me. Why on God's green Earth do medical suppliers still design them this way?)

"Oh, yeah, they are a bit odd, sorry about that. You can just tuck the whole thing into your underwear and put on a regular pad when you get home. Remember, no tampons for the next two weeks, okay?" I thought I was clear, but apparently not as she gave me a blank stare. I was used to pretty profound shock by many young patients when they learned that they would have to forgo tampons for bulky maxi pads, so I paid no mind as I continued my work.

Blaze continued to look quizzically at the pad in her hand. There was no embarrassment in her tone when she finally replied, "I didn't wear any underwear today."

Another stumper for me. I paged one of the recovery room nurses to see if they had any suggestions on how to handle this. Without one exchange of wonderment at a patient who thought she could drift in to have an abortion and just slip her sundress over her head and leave, we tried to come up with some sort of solution. The result was comical, but leave it to the never-ending ingenuity of nurses to rig up a diaper made out of disposable underpads and surgical tape.

Without a trace of self-consciousness, Blaze gratefully accepted our handiwork and waddled out of the clinic with conspicuous lumps under her diaphanous flowing sundress. In my estimation, that was one of my better days.

Brandi

I was on a thunderously busy roll, as usual, when I motioned patient number 13 and her mom into my office from the back hallway. As the pale, freckle-faced teen sat down with her mom glued to her side, I scanned her chart. Fourteen years old, first pregnancy, seven weeks and three days pregnant according to her ultrasound. Twins. I began my usual spiel and started with the usual barrage of medical questions: Any allergies? Any past medical problems? Any family history of heart disease, cancer, diabetes? Everything zipped by with negative answers until the last question.

"Oh, well, my father and grandfather has had two heart attacks." Brandi brushed her wispy bangs off her forehead as she dutifully piped up with this information.

"Which one, your father or your grandfather?" I asked, barely looking up from the history and physical examination form in front of me.

"My father *is* my grandfather," she replied.

I paused with my pen in midair, confused for a few seconds until it slowly dawned on me. I looked up, and as I did, I saw Brandi staring blankly as her mother looked me in the eye, pleased that I was catching on.

"Yes, her grandfather is also her father. My father raped me when I was a teenager and I had her." She nodded pointedly at her daughter. "And now he raped Brandi, and she's pregnant."

As these words were spoken, I was stunned into trying to keep my composure as the mom clearly verified what I was slowly putting together. What was equally astonishing was the level-headed delivery of such information. I mustered my most calm, professional demeanor and pressed on with the rest of the questions as the bile slid up into my throat. I hoped that my hands weren't too shaky as I did a quick exam, checking her vital signs, listening to her heart and lungs, and checking for anything out of the ordinary that would merit a call to the anesthesiologist or doctor as a heads-up before surgery. Amazingly, this child—save for a broad forehead, pronounced overbite, and slow answers—was in seemingly good health.

And now for the tough part. "So, what is the plan for all of this? Did you press criminal charges?"

"Oh no, it was really just an accident. My dad and her grand-dad didn't really have sex with her. Not gonna lie, he was getting too close to her, but it didn't actually go in," her mom confided easily through broken teeth while Brandi just looked down at the tiled floor. "So, you know, it's fair to say she's still a virgin. Ain't that right, Brandi?"

Brandi nodded mutely.

"Um, could you excuse me for a minute?" was all I could manage to get out before standing up.

"Oh, if you're goin' to see the director, she already knows."

"Okay, I just need to double-check on some things. I'll be right back." I scurried out of that room in a cold sweat as I took off down the hall to Marilyn's office.

Marilyn was in her office talking on the phone and motioned me to sit down. I was far too agitated and grossed out to sit after what had just happened. She finally hung up and looked at me quizzically. This wasn't the first time I had stormed into her office to pace around, nor would it be the last.

"OH MY GOD, OH MY GOD!" I wrung my hands and doubled over on the back of the chair she had offered me, dry heaving a little. "That little girl was raped by her *grandpa*! And he raped the mom too!" I wailed as I tried to keep my voice down. The walls were surprisingly thin in that place.

"I know, it's horrible," Marilyn said with her usual unflappable veneer.

"How do we handle this?!"

"Well, I just got off the phone with their social worker who referred them here. This family is well known to the county welfare system, and they've been working with them for years. The mom never wants to press charges, but with the girl being only fourteen, they're finally able to get the police involved. It's horrible, I know," she repeated.

"Okay, well, I can honestly say that I have *never* been happier to help a patient have an abortion. Thanks." I took my shaken self back down the hall and took a few deep breaths before entering my office where the two of them sat patiently. I still had the birth control counseling to do.

I almost never allowed a parent or a guardian to listen in on this conversation, and most especially not in circumstances such as these. I asked the mom to leave while I finished up with Brandi. Naturally, she resisted, saying she was there to help her daughter. I kindly but firmly told her that she needed to step out, and she finally did so reluctantly. As she walked out, it surprised me when I sensed her deep concern for her daughter. She was very aware of the shame and trauma of several generations of incest, and I could really feel her fear for her daughter as she left helplessly.

What a strange, tragic folding together of family dynamics that had led to this unspeakable situation. I will never, ever forget it. And lest you try to comfort yourself by thinking, *Oh, well, that was a long time ago*, I can assure you that squirming is still in order since my niece, a physical therapist, encountered an even more horrific case just last year. All I will tell you about that case is that it is an ongoing saga of several generations of incest and abuse in a very, very disturbing house. And yes, social services is doing their best, which is clearly not nearly enough.

"Brandi, you have been through an awful lot. I am so sorry to hear about everything that has happened to you," I said carefully. "I want you to know that we are working to help you. Okay?"

"Yeah, okay, thank you," she said stutteringly.

"Now, do you want some birth control so you don't get pregnant again?" I asked. She looked at me uncertainly. I cleared my throat and tried again. "I mean, I know your grandfather probably won't be allowed to go near you, but do you have a boyfriend or someone else? You have to be careful because you can get pregnant again right away."

"Um, yeah, I do have a boyfriend, so I guess I should try to get some protection."

We talked about which method would be best, given that her mom was pretty intrusive, and settled on the Depo-Provera injection, which would keep her safe for a couple of months. I exhaled a huge sigh of relief as I directed her to her mom and the next phase of preoperative services at the cashier's office. Thankfully, I soon overheard Anna Maria discussing use of the emergency funds that she carefully accessed in the direst of situations.

My hands are shaking as I recall this most horrifying of stories so many years later. To say that I withhold judgment for the man who committed such atrocities would be impossible. Although I deeply believe that the only way out of these generational patterns is to explore the psyche of men who do these things, I am not the person for the job. It takes a unique individual indeed to be able to maintain their role as a neutral witness as they dive deeply into the sinister and violent inner worlds of the perpetrators of rape and incest. To walk alongside these souls requires a specific sort of genius that is desperately needed if humankind truly wants to eradicate this very real phenomenon from the lexicon of human behavior.

As a general rule, you will find that most medical professionals can tell these stories calmly to illustrate a point, and I am no different. I have told this story in class to nursing students and am able to do so without much more than gulping a bit when recounting it. Being able to role model self-control is a really important teaching tool, and I remember certain moments as a nursing student when I benefited greatly from my instructors as they told stories like these with the intent of not only teaching but also demonstrating composure.

This is not about showing off how tough you are. It is critically important to develop this skill in order to function effectively in horrific circumstances. It appears that most people enjoy seeing this in action on popular TV programs, and from the little

I've watched, they are also hugely entertained in the aftermath as traumatized doctors and nurses cry, laugh, commit suicide, or tumble into bed together to cope with what they've witnessed. I really wouldn't know. I don't watch those shows.

ELEVEN

High School Days

high school [ˈhī ˌsko͞ol]_(n) *Where self-esteem, inno-cence, and dreams go to die.*
                                                    —**Internet meme**

ABOUT A YEAR INTO my employment, Marilyn asked me to help her with some of the never-ending demands on her time. As a former hospital nurse educator, I was happy to take a break once in a while from the rigors of patient care to do something different. As I may have mentioned, I was—and still am—always up for a good clerical challenge that might involve sitting down and organizing computer files or even stuffing envelopes to rest my weary mind (and feet).

"How can I help?" I asked.

"Well, the regional high school asked me if someone could come and do a short presentation about contraception and abortion for their health class next Tuesday. Would you mind doing it?"

"Oh, I would be happy to! I love that stuff!" I responded, genuinely pleased at the thought of informally meeting in a class-room with a few teenagers to talk about something that would really interest them. My own sex-ed classes when I was in high school were taught by the gym teachers, and you could always tell that they dreaded teaching this stuff as they bravely plowed through the material in a bored manner designed to shut down any questions from the class. Looking back, I really can't blame them—it seems to me the oddest thing. Who thought it would be a good idea to take a person who is far more skilled at teaching volleyball or tennis and compel them to stand in front of a bunch of slides and explain the male and female reproductive systems? Worse yet, then expect them to translate that into how to safely navigate sexual health in the real world? How painfully inadequate!

Inadequate, maybe, but the saddest thing of all, to me, is when adolescents do not even get the benefit of learning the basics. What's going on here?

When I started researching the current state of sexual educa-tion for today's youth in the United States of America, I had to step away. I knew it was bad, but not *this* bad. As the product of public-school education in the early 80s, I have been blissfully unaware of this sad state of affairs. I knew that conservatism had swung many states to successfully wipe out sex ed from schools altogether, but I guess I just chose to focus on the myriad oth-er social and personal issues that have consumed my attention in recent years. I suspect educators have had to do the same. Really, you have to pick your battles. I, for one, cannot imagine being a school superintendent who has to steel myself before rowdy Board of Education meetings to try to convince people why it might be unwise to issue guns to teachers let alone convince parents that their kids should be taught how to behave responsibly in their bedrooms or in the backs of cars. And yes, if you are a non-U.S. citizen reading this book, I see you shaking your head in disbelief.

To be honest, I am really impressed that kids are doing as well as they are with getting the information that they need, at least as far as outcomes. Between 1991 and 2015, the teen birth rate dropped 64 percent.[27] Although experts are not willing to say so, I suspect that internet access has tons to do with teens figuring out how to avoid pregnancy. That and the massively popular preteen book series *A Series of Unfortunate Events*, where the main characters are kids who cleverly and courageously learn to navigate their world because every single adult is outrageously incompetent. Ditto for the TV series *South Park*. Here is one benefit to the internet age: while kids may not be taught in schools directly, they have access to some really excellent information out there. Of course, that is not to say that they are always accessing reliable resources, but at least they can find information if they try.

However, lest you get excited about the mixed blessing that is the internet for our precious children, do be aware that the United States still has the highest teen birth rate in the industrialized world. The data is undisputable in convincing us that this is not something to be proud of. Teens who become parents are more likely to become high school dropouts, experience poverty, and be connected to child welfare and correctional systems.[28] And here are some fun facts about kids and sexual activity: in 2017, the CDC reported that 40 percent of high school kids have had sex, with 54 percent reporting that they used condoms, and 30 percent using other methods like birth control pills or IUDs during their most recent sexual encounter.[29]

As for sexually transmitted infections (STIs), it's a lowball estimate (due to underreporting) that one out of every four sexually active adolescent females is reported to have an STI at any given time. So, figure it's probably closer to one in three. Wow. And parents, if you think that loading your kids' schedules from morning to night with sports, clubs, and the like will make them too tired for anything else, think again. I still chuckle in amazement at the 15-year-old, complete with frizzy brown hair and thick glasses, who managed to find time to get pregnant the very first time she had sex despite her impossibly busy schedule of 5:00 a.m. swim team followed by school, afterschool math club, and honors-level homework.

While these tidbits of information are kind of disturbing, what made me throw up my hands to stomp downstairs and rant at my poor husband were the numbers regarding sex education in our fine public institutions. I had thought that only privately educated kids, particularly those in Christian-based schools, got virtually *no* information other than that God wanted them to save it for marriage. What really made me crazy is that many states' public schools, as mentioned above, have bailed on our kids too. I guess it's probably more of a priority to teach them how not to get gunned down during lunch period in the cafeteria at this point, but I digress. As of April 2022, only 26 states plus the District of Columbia currently mandate sex education and HIV education in public schools, and get this: a mere 18 require that if it *is* provided, sex and/or HIV education must be medically, factually, or technically accurate.[30] I am not making this up, although I wish I were.

In retrospect, I am certainly glad that I did not know any of this before my trip to the high school, hoping that the kids would see me as a credible adult. I figured that I would gather some information that they could relate to followed by an engaging Q&A session that would be refereed by a teacher who knew how to rein in the troublemakers. I prepared some slides, brought in a couple of pill packs and an IUD, and tried not to dress like a hopelessly unfashionable middle-aged nurse, which I kind of was.

So, imagine my chagrin when, by the first-period bell at 8:07 a.m., I found myself not in a classroom but in the massive high school auditorium being introduced over the microphone to a full house of around 500 students. They shuffled in, and some even displayed mild interest in the dog-and-pony proceedings of the day, having—just the week before—sat through a presentation by a man from the National Right to Life Committee, the nation's oldest anti-abortion group, which was founded by the Catholic Church.

It seemed that the school's administrators had failed to tell me that I was *not* going to be giving the small health class talks that I had prepared. Rather, I was there as part of a series on controversial social issues of the day. The educators solicited guest speakers on a variety of topics and would have a person representing one side of a controversial topic come one week while someone from the opposing side would present the following week. I gave them credit for what was surely an interesting and informative mandatory course for all students but felt a little blindsided by this setup.

I had no choice but to wing it with what I had prepared. I gave a disclaimer that I was a nurse, not a policy expert, and so I would not be talking about the sociopolitical implications of contraception and abortion, just the clinical perspective. To my resounding relief, the students seemed to be very much impressed by my street cred as someone who works on the front line. It should have come as no surprise since most people, especially young ones, are sick and tired of hearing from those who don't actually work in the fields that they so expertly discuss.

Sorry, pundits, you've been outed. I do feel your pain; I myself have been seen as less than credible when I have been perceived, particularly by nursing students, as hopelessly out of touch. Even though it would've been even cooler if I had worn scrubs and a stethoscope, I realized that the students felt I was the right person for the job at hand, so I did my best to explain what they wanted to hear. What they were after was the real scoop from the clinic around the corner, not a theoretical lecture from some out-of-touch administrator.

I stuck to my original script, and to my surprise, the students were engaged and thoughtful in their questions, even though they often strayed to topics I could not address.

"Why don't they teach us this stuff in regular class?"

I leaned toward the microphone and cleared my throat. "I am guessing you probably got a lot of this information in health class, but maybe you just don't remember." An exasperated gym teacher with a whistle around her neck nodded vigorously.

"Why did that old White guy last week say that you can get cancer from having an abortion?"

"I can only tell you that this notion comes from a really old study done in the seventies that's been proven not to be accurate."

"Why is it that you can get an abortion without your parents' consent, but they have to sign to let you get your ears pierced?"

"Oh, wow, I didn't know that!" I said. The audience broke out in laughter and whispering until the teachers shushed them. "Seriously, though, I *do* know that in this state, kids seeking birth control and abortion do not need their parents' consent to go to the clinic or the doctor, so it's important that you all know that. Sorry about the piercing thing." Chuckles all around. I was *killing* it!

"Why should we believe what you're saying, anyway? People keep coming in here and they all say something different." This from a moody-looking teen in the back row.

"Good question! I don't know what to tell you. I can only speak about what it's like when you go out into the real world as a patient."

Before I knew it, the requisite 42 minutes was up, and I got 3 whole minutes to gather myself and take a few sips of water before the next 500 kids slouched in. I had never seen so many nose rings and purple-haired individuals in one place before. The day proceeded in this whirlwind fashion for the entire six periods, broken in the middle by a quick 20-minute lunch break that the teachers kindly treated me to in the huge cafeteria swarming with kids. The noise was deafening as they tried to make polite small talk over tater tots and macaroni and cheese. I even got a chocolate chip cookie for dessert!

I am telling you the truth when I say that I have never had a more emotionally and physically exhausting day. I come from a family of teachers, and I salute them all. Far be it from me to ever say that these fine people do not have one of the toughest and most important jobs in the world. I never got invited back, but it's not clear if that's because they do the same topics every year and I didn't make the grade or if they moved on to other pressing concerns. It really doesn't matter. I feel certain that at least a few of the students were appreciative of my time and effort.

I know that these kids, who by now are well into adulthood, muddled through as best they could—as we all do through life—and hopefully they'll do their best to give their own kids a shot at being able to find credible, reliable information. As for me, I think of how my academic mentor always reminded his students of the old adage, "People won't remember what you told them, but they will certainly remember how you made them feel." I can only hope that, if nothing else, those hundreds of kids felt respected in that moment for whatever choices were theirs to make in life.

TWELVE

Nurses

gal·lows hu·mor /ˈgalōz ˈ(h)yo͞omər/
noun
1. grim and ironic humor in a desperate or
    hopeless situation.[31]

ONCE AGAIN, I RUN the very real risk of offending more than one reader as I delve into the next part of my story. For anyone who treasures the notion of the sanctity of life, I am here to tell you that I do too, in spite of the very blasphemous tales that I am about to tell. It makes me think about the title of a very cool book, *Nurses' Work, The Sacred and The Profane*, by Zane Robinson Wolf. Just yesterday, a good friend casually related how her hearing aid fell out and almost got swallowed up in some woman's vagina as she assisted her in childbirth. Of course, I giggled insanely, and it made my day.

The infamous gallows humor of nursing is, to me, less about grimness or hopelessness than it is about the deliciously juicy tightrope walk between the sacred and the profane. Nurses straddle the thin line between joy and grief, purity and filth, and also the comedy and tragedy of life. We learn to adapt to rapidly changing situations in the wink of an eye as we go from patient to patient, switching gears as we enter people's private worlds every time we step into an exam room or pull a curtain aside. This ability informs the stuff you see on popular television medical shows, with their snarky banter or melodramatic angst.

I cannot find it in myself to watch characters on TV like Nurse Jackie, whose antics my students loved to describe to me as she broke a different moral code in each episode with her spot-on know-how and subsequent prurient behavior. Likewise, the insanely pure and selfless stereotypes conjured from inaccurate but commonly held beliefs about Florence Nightingale make me simultaneously cringe and straighten my shoulders with pride. Like all of my colleagues, I am all of those things, and I am none of them.

Which brings me to the fun of telling you about Amber. About three years into my tenure, the newish administrator, Kim, introduced me to the new RN she had hired. I beheld a pleasantly plump, clear-skinned, tousled blonde who vivaciously pumped my hand in greeting.

"Oh my gosh, I am *so* excited to meet you! I know we're gonna be best buddies in no time!" Cautiously amused, I returned her handshake, walked her through the clinic, and outlined what her responsibilities would be.

I soon discovered every last thing about Amber's background as she cheerfully spilled her guts during her orientation. She was a new grad just out of her associate degree program who had admirably toiled her way through the rigors of nursing school while working and being a single mom of an adorable and very active seven-year-old boy. Despite her bubbly dizziness, I could see that she was no dummy. Twirling her thick, wavy tresses, she was able to calculate intravenous drip rates and medication dosages with ease.

As we finished our orientation, Amber sized me up and unexpectedly blurted, "You know, you could really make a fortune as a dancer." I glanced down briefly at my scrubs-clad body and marveled at the inappropriateness of this declaration in a busy health-care setting.

"Umm, I never really thought about that. Thanks," I mumbled uncomfortably. This was a very weird conversation. Despite my desire to move on from this awkwardness, for a moment I envisioned myself leaping and twirling with utmost grace and precision as I floated across the stage playing the role of one of the enviably elegant ballerinas in *Swan Lake*. (*See, Mom? I knew you should've given me dance lessons, but no, you said it would be a waste of money!*) But wait... ballerinas are famously underpaid, aren't they? *Oh dear, Amber means another form of dancing, I think.*

"Yeah, no, I mean it!" Amber continued. "I am taking a huge pay cut becoming a nurse, but, oh well, I guess it's worth it. I won't be thirty forever. I could totally get you in on a few good gigs, though, if you want to make some money on the side."

"So, were you a stripper?"

"Oh please, *no*. I worked in a club as an exotic dancer, but it was a nice one, you know? The hours sucked, and my back started killing me after too many shifts, but it was all legit. I'd make a couple grand in a weekend." Amber looked about as exotic as

Miss Cornhusker 2001 from Omaha, Nebraska.

I started to giggle at the thought of quickly paying off my mortgage after telling my husband and kids that "Mommy's gotta work weekends and don't ask me why I need to jump around the house in nine-inch stilettos to strengthen my ankles."

"Oh my *god*, Amber, how old do you think I *am*?"

"Well, you know, lots of girls dance, and you can't really tell their age," Amber offered. Giving me a wink, she leaned in and said, "I've got a totally foolproof new gig opening up. It's really gonna take off, I'm telling you! Online stuff, all the rage, and you can name your own hours!"

"Oh, wow, that sounds, um, lucrative, but I'll pass."

"Okay, suit yourself. It's gonna be awesome!"

Once the rest of the staff got to know Amber, it was no holds barred. Her good-natured exhibitionism was met with everything from incredulity to salivation, at least from some of the older anesthesiologists. She flounced and flirted her way through every day, a true girlfriend to patients in need, with lots of pointers on hair and makeup to perk them up after a harrowing experience. Practical jokes that garnered more attention were all part of the fun. A pink vibrator peeking out from under a drape or an adorable teddy bear with its legs splayed ready for a go on an operating room table was always met with a jovial chuckle. Needless to say, our more serious social-justice-warrior staff were not amused.

What got her fired was the last straw. I arrived for my afternoon shift to find everyone in a shaken, somber mood, except the imperturbable Nurse Liz, who never missed a beat. Kim pulled me into her office to explain that, early in the day, there had been a bomb threat. You'd think this would be a fairly common occurrence given the nature of our business, but it was the first and only time that patients and staff had to be evacuated that I had experienced.

"Where's Amber?" I wondered out loud as the staff was finishing up with the last of the day's cases before I started seeing postsurgical follow-ups.

"Oh, you know, shakin' her ass on the hood of White Snake's car," Liz sang in a throaty voice as Kim shushed her with a withering look and led me to her office. Kim didn't even bother to close her door. "I had to fire her today. She came in just as we were evacuating patients, found out about the bomb threat, turned around, and walked right out the door. Not attempting to save anyone but herself is grounds for immediate termination, as I'm sure you know."

Well, actually, I didn't, not having worked anywhere this nuts before, but okay, that makes sense. I started to giggle, and Kim, after a shocked moment, joined me after I couldn't resist sharing my vision of Miss Thing parading in, looking around, and firmly marching right back out still clutching her oversized Powerpuff Girls key chain to wade through the throng of surgical personnel, pink gowns, and paper booties in the parking lot, then go shrieking down the driveway in her yellow Jeep. It's the little things that make your day.

THIRTEEN

Weighing The Risks

"There are risks and costs to action. But they are far less than the long range risks of comfortable inaction."

—John F. Kennedy, *The Uncommon Wisdom of JFK*

SO FAR, I'VE BEEN telling you about the more than 98 percent of women who are absolutely fine after an abortion. Of the remaining 2 percent, most complications are considered minor, such as infection or bleeding.[32] You may be a little curious about the less than 1 percent who do experience serious complications. There is absolutely no denying that legal abortion is as safe as it is common, but as with any medical procedure, there is always the possibility of injury from the surgical procedure itself.[33]

Today, it is important to note that postoperative infection has been nearly eradicated; providers have dramatically improved outcomes by giving a single-dose antibiotic immediately after surgery. Back in my day at the women's clinic, I saw and helped manage the extremely rare post-procedure infection, but

I personally never saw an injury from a surgical instrument. The reasons for infection were many: early return to sexual activity, unsanitary conditions, or patients not taking their postoperative antibiotic for a variety of reasons that could fill a book. I also cared for a few heavy bleeders, but again, they were quite the minority. Postoperative hemorrhage is most commonly associated with multiple previous pregnancies, underlying conditions like fibroids, or partially retained pregnancy tissue. Repeat surgical evacuation is often performed in these cases to ensure removal of clots or tissue which promotes uterine healing and return to prepregnancy size.[34]

Only once did we have to send a patient emergently to the hospital. This young woman had an undiagnosed weakness in her uterine wall, and sadly, her uterus ruptured. This almost certainly would also have happened if the pregnancy had progressed. She survived the event, but we later learned that the hospital doctors had been unable to repair the weak area that had torn, and she would never be able to bear more children.

It is widely known among health-care providers that the risks associated with carrying a pregnancy to full term are far greater than those from an abortion. According to the Centers for Disease Control, 700 women in the U.S. die each year in childbirth, with an overall rate of about 8 percent experiencing a risk of serious complications.[35] Moral and religious issues aside, it is far safer for a woman to have an abortion than to carry a pregnancy full term, with a mere 0.23 percent chance of serious complications from abortion[36] as opposed to an 8 percent chance from full-term pregnancy.[37]

I don't like to get melodramatic here in extrapolating the

numbers and saying there is an almost an eight-fold chance of serious complication and death if you choose to have a baby, since the odds for remaining healthy are still pretty good for either choice, but the bottom line is irrefutable from a medical standpoint: for women, having a baby is riskier than not.[38]

To be sure, it's clear that these numbers reflect maternal health and have absolutely nothing to do with a baby's point of view, which is at the crux of the pro-life stance no matter how they try to state otherwise. The moral and philosophical implications of carrying a pregnancy to term versus choosing to terminate are immense and, as all good citizens who aren't currently living under a rock know by now, intensely and endlessly debated. I stand firm in my stance that my job here is not to debate this, only to bring to light the medical facts surrounding abortion.

FOURTEEN

Heidi

"We who choose to surround ourselves with lives even more temporary than our own live within a fragile circle; easily and often breached. Unable to accept its awful gaps, we would still live no other way. We cherish memory as the only certain immortality, never fully understanding the necessary plan."

—Irving Townsend, *Separate Lifetimes*

ONE DAY, A SPRIGHTLY 33-year-old patient came into my office with a sad smile and charming accent. As probably the ninth person that day to ask her where she was from and then comment, "Ooh, I *love* your accent!" I knew it was trite and tiresome, but I couldn't resist. Turned out she was from New Zealand and had recently moved here with her husband and two kids. He had gotten a job in the city, and they had found a nice place in the burbs to raise their kids.

Heidi had a background in health care. Back in New Zealand, she went through college and trained as a medical technologist. She worked for several years in a lab analyzing tissue samples and was the very important person who would examine and give preliminary findings on biopsies. Having almost chosen medical technology over nursing as a career myself, I sometimes think about the people who look at slides under microscopes all day finding everything from routine infections to advanced cancer. Given my penchant for human interaction and a wide range of experiences, I am quite satisfied with my choice but still carry enormous admiration for these fine, meticulous lab personnel.

As Heidi settled into the chair, Marilyn popped her head in. "Patrice, can I see you a moment?"

I stepped outside my office and shut the door. "What's up?"

"Well, let me know what you think about Heidi after you talk to her. She said she's a medical technologist and might want to work here." Marilyn was always on the lookout for potential hires. As you might imagine, it can be quite a challenge in the abortion field to find qualified, interested candidates. I don't think I've ever worked in a place where I was expected to conduct a patient history and physical examination that included assessing employment potential, but I guess I've done weirder things.

Heidi passed her interviews and surgery with flying colors. In no time at all, she was welcomed onto the team. It was a bit odd to see her in our teal-colored scrubs so soon after the pinkish-orange gown, but her sunny disposition and solid work performance soon put everyone at ease. The lab was adjacent to the discharge lounge where, at the end of the day, I would give patients some much-appreciated snacks and go over their instructions one more time before they headed out the door.

Before they could leave, I had to get the okay from the lab technician that the fetal tissue was all present and accounted for.

You may remember that there is a small but significant danger of severe hemorrhage from retained tissue. The POC (products of conception) are also inspected for any abnormalities that might merit a patient discussion, such as something like a hydatidiform mole, a somewhat rare pregnancy that is characterized by a dissolving fetus surrounded by a tumor that can be a precursor to later uterine cancer. After a quick analysis in the clinic, the tissue would be sent to an outside lab and we would get a detailed pathology report for each patient. It would usually merely identify normal findings for any given gestational age, but every now and again there would be a finding that warranted a call to the patient to urge further follow-up. Abnormal findings, as the above-mentioned molar pregnancy or overt genetic malformations could be a precursor to future problems. At that time, after the report was completed, all tissue was disposed of as medical waste.

As a side note, there has been monumental change in the United States following massive controversy about fetal remains in the last five years or so. You may remember the now famously edited videos released in 2015 by the anti-abortion group the Center for Medical Progress, which stirred up a hornet's nest of controversy in falsely portraying abortion providers selling fetal tissue to research companies for a profit.[39] As a result, there has been a fascinating trend in recent U.S. history to acknowledge and dignify aborted fetuses with what many believe is a proper burial.

A number of states now require women to make decisions

regarding burial or cremation of their fetuses, and providers have had to develop new working relationships with funeral homes across the country.[40] Many see this as an outrageous pro-life push to cause a huge guilt trip, not to mention increased fees and adding undue stress in an already difficult situation.

While I see their point, personally, I am not so sure it is the worst thing in the world. On many occasions, my colleagues and I often remarked that we wished the experience was less impersonal and detached in a way that would help people grieve and honor the experience as well as promote deeper introspection. I see this as an opportunity for healing, not only for the many women I saw who breezed in with no apparent concern for the gravity of the situation but for those who struggle in silence and shame as well. In researching this further, I am a big fan of what they're doing in the United Kingdom—a lovely website from the British Pregnancy Advisory Council encourages thoughtful decision-making, including how women can opt to take their fetal remains home in an opaque biodegradable container so they can dispose of them in an individually meaningful way, with lots of suggestions on how to do so.[41]

I enjoyed working closely alongside Heidi as I learned a lot about her life and cultural background. I also very much relished her down-to-earth observations about our peculiar American culture that so often seemed perfectly normal to me. She was forever perplexed by little and not-so-little quirks, like why we must have 17 kinds of mushrooms at the grocery store but go into massive debt paying for college. One of her most poignant learning experiences came from a nosy neighbor who called child protective services to complain about her and her husband leaving their four- and six-year-old children alone for 15 minutes each day as there was a small gap in time when one parent had to leave and the other would arrive home from work.

"Why on Earth would someone call the authorities about something like that?" she wondered aloud, distraught at the thought of her precious kids being taken away from her for something so ridiculous.

"Well, in the United States, we have very strict guidelines for never leaving a child unattended, even for a few minutes," I offered, surprised that this may not be so in other places.

"Oh, for heaven's sake! I always leave them with a snack and stuff to do, and they know how to call us if there is a problem," she said.

"I know, but people are really funny about it. They worry that something bad could happen in an instant," I noted.

"Okay, but if they are worried, then why don't they offer to help?"

I was stumped.

Unfortunately, Heidi worked at the clinic for only about six months. If you have a queasy stomach, I suggest that you skip ahead a bit as I describe why. For this is the gruesome telling of the part of the abortion story that everyone, including myself, dreads when they think about it in the physical sense. It is all well and good to examine the lives of the women who, for myriad reasons, choose to end a pregnancy, as I've done so far. But as for the tiny beings that pro-lifers wring their hands and tear their hair out obsessing over, it surely wouldn't be fair not to give a nod to the fetuses, those symbols of hope unfulfilled in their precarious shot at embodying a human life.

Let me just pause here and tell you a story that might make you feel better if you do choose to skip the rest of Heidi's story. When I was a young, hip, big-city hospital nurse with a few years under my belt, I had the extraordinary privilege of being followed by none other than Peggy Anderson, the award-winning author of the book *Nurse*, a 1979 novel that won critical acclaim and was the basis for a hit TV series in the '80s starring Michael Learned. Peggy had decided that her next project would be to write a book about newly graduated nurses and their struggles in their first year on the job. Working with hospital administrators, she was able to select three new grads that I was orienting and gained permission to follow us as we did our jobs.

She would stand discreetly outside of patient rooms with her notepad and only asked questions during breaks. Clearly, this was long before HIPAA was enacted to protect any and all patient information. However, I can tell you that she, along with all of us, felt a strong sense of moral obligation to respect and honor the fact that the stories were more about the new nurses than any patients. I am sometimes saddened at how very difficult it is to get the public to understand our work in this day and age of confidentiality to the point of dark secrecy, but it really is the best alternative we have at the moment.

Peggy would listen with rapt attention to our teaching sessions at the bedside. I found out later that she had never actually set foot in the hospital when she wrote *Nurse*. She amazingly wrote this detailed and emotional book from a series of interviews she had had with the lead character, a real nurse who would go on to become her dear friend. So, this was her first foray amid the sights, sounds, and smells of real hospital care.

She covered her jitters pretty well, I'd say.

One day, I was happy to learn during the morning shift report that my newbies would get to do some postmortem care on a patient who had just died. We had a checklist of procedures that we wanted every orientee to experience, and this was one that we couldn't always get easily. You'd be surprised how many dying people wait until night shift to take their leave.

Peggy trotted obediently behind us as we gathered supplies and talked about how to prepare a body for the morgue. My one orientee, Steve, was pretty nervous, and I had to help him steady himself before we went into the room. We did our job respectfully but efficiently, with me instructing them clearly how to tie the jaw shut, to be sure to place the incontinence pad under them as fluids spilled out freely, and, oh, not to forget the toe tag before securing the shroud. Steve was shaky but he made it through okay.

When we exited the room, Peggy was nowhere to be found. Shaken to the core by what she had witnessed, she never returned after that day, and the book that she'd spent months researching never got written. Many nurses later rolled their eyes and shrugged at such weakness, but I had grown to respect Peggy and was truly sorry that she had been so unprepared and deeply distressed. Most people in the Western world never have the opportunity to participate in a death, and it is a real shame that we've sanitized it to the point that it is outside the realm of normal human experience.

Back to Heidi. While late-term abortions were fairly rare, we did occasionally do them up to 24 weeks into a pregnancy as was allowed by state law. Those laws have been hotly contested in the last few years, particularly as questions have arisen over the viability of a fetus to survive outside the womb due to dramatic advances in neonatal medicine. These late-term procedures required a lot more stages, and the patients were heavily counseled every step of the way. They were—and are still—extremely expensive, and can cost upward of five thousand dollars or even more depending on the circumstances.[42] The patient would have to come in several times to get gradual cervical dilation before the surgery could take place, and they were almost always surprised to learn that they would likely have to deal with breast milk coming in just as they would if they carried to term.

What kind of person would wait so long to decide to have an abortion? I'll start you off with the suggestion, of all things, to check out a reality TV show aptly called *I Didn't Know I Was Pregnant* to get an idea of how this can happen, although if you want a more credible explanation, I urge you to read the fine work that *The Atlantic* journalists have done in bringing real women's abortion stories to light.[43] As for the television show, while I cannot substantiate the truth of any of these women's stories, they sure sounded familiar when I watched some episodes a few years ago. Irregular periods, sudden breakups, and the dread of telling parents are among the many scenarios that drive women to seek second-trimester abortions. Also consider the grim fact that more than a third of all domestic violence starts or gets worse when a woman is pregnant. In fact, 15 percent of all women report experiencing violence during their pregnancies, and 40 to 60 percent of all women experiencing domestic violence are abused while they are pregnant.[44] It should surprise no one that a pregnant woman might change her mind when it becomes clear that she is in a dangerous situation.

While these cases are never easy in any way, we had one that was disturbing enough that Heidi, much like Peggy Anderson, vanished that very same day, never to return.

Despite intense counseling about her options, a young woman decided firmly that she wanted to terminate her 20-week pregnancy, which consisted of twins. When those two fetuses arrived in the lab, they looked very recognizable indeed. It was really, really hard for me as well, and, not for the first time, I said a little prayer for the little lives that might have been.

I assure you, seeing fetuses in various stages of development lined up in surgical trays was not always easy. If you want a genuine sense of what this looks like in real life as opposed to the glamour shots you see in pro-life materials, I urge you to watch *The Abortion Divide*, the excellent documentary from 2019 on PBS *Frontline* that bravely investigates the state of affairs regarding abortion in recent years. The filmmakers were permitted in the lab of an actual abortion clinic, and you can draw your own conclusions as you see the lab techs analyzing nine-week fetal tissue up close and personal.

I am in awe not only of the clinic but also of the filmmakers for sharing this so freely. It is only through this kind of transparency that we can come to a true understanding of what actually happens in order for each of us to be able to process and shape our personal feelings around this issue. In my experience, it's pretty difficult to ascertain various structures unless you are a trained ultrasonographer or laboratory technician. But at the heart of it, that is neither here nor there because, as I said earlier, it is *all* miraculous, every bit of it. To come to terms with the beauty and loss of life in all its facets is to be fully, completely, heartbreakingly human.

Even before the experience that scared Heidi away, I had gone to the minister at my church to talk about my initial discomfort with seeing itty-bitty fetuses lined up in shallow glass trays for analysis. I was an active member of the Unitarian Universalist Church just down the road. If you're not familiar with this religion, it is a liberal congregation that espouses a "free and responsible search for truth and meaning."[45] I would love to say that my wise and scholarly older minister assuaged my doubts, but that would be far from the truth. He offered wonderfully heart-centered listening and knowledge of various spiritual beliefs about what it means to be alive, but I had to look deep inside myself for healing the pain and confusion I had around my experiences. I can only suggest that each of you do the same.

I have come to understand that life is a complex interplay between physical and nonphysical forms, that it comes and goes as easily as a puff of wind that breathes momentary life into a fluff of dandelion seed as it dances merrily before settling back into the Earth. Whether it finds a home in the fertile ground or it bounces hard on an inhospitable bit of concrete is of no concern to it on its primordial quest. Life exists in an endless, undulating tangle of potential, rich aliveness and death.

FIFTEEN

An Eclectic Mix Of Memories

"Variety is the very spice of life that gives it all its flavor."
—William Cowper, "The Task"

STORIES, NOT FACES, BURBLE up through the cracks of my consciousness as I brush my teeth, wash dishes, or fold laundry far more readily than when I sit down and press my brain for more examples. These gems shimmer on the edge of my memory—long ago people who managed to show up every day in every clinic, prototypes for the recurring scenarios that still run riot in our culture. I share these stories to emphasize for you, just a little more, the wide array of people who flowed through the clinic doors and continue to do so today.

Prisoners

I would like to give you faces to put with the names, but the truth is that all of the prisoners I've ever cared for presented in the same manner—faces frozen in stony submission as they were guided in wearing their orange jumpsuits, ankles and wrists shackled and clanking for all the world to see and hear. If they were sometimes diverted through the back hallway entrance, it was only to avoid rattling the nerves of the other patients. The guards, some kind and some not, would hustle the women into the room and usually look for something on the exam table that they could lock their chains onto in order to foil an escape.

It was surprising how often these unfortunate women were escorted by male guards. Why is that *ever* a good idea? The men would shuffle in, eyes downcast, and silently do their job. They visibly squirmed or offered weak protest whenever I asked them to please unbind the ankles so that I could perform an exam. This often invoked a saucy I-told-you-so smirk from the inmate.

I learned how to ask the right questions to get what I needed. There were always two guards, so I would pull one aside and ask if it was okay to leave the patient alone with me, or with me and a female attendant. This was also a great time to find out a little more about the circumstances surrounding their incarceration and pregnancy. Getting accurate info was hit or miss, but worth a try.

Most clinicians will tell you that they have almost never felt unsafe caring for a prisoner, and I am no different. They were deferential, respectful, and glad to get some outside help even if it didn't really meet their needs. As a dear colleague once pointed out, these are not the people you worry about; it's the unexpected loonies who come in jacked up and at the end of their rope that'll get you every time. You learn to scan for that recognizable look in the eyes, crazed and either diffuse or razor sharp.

As with 99 percent of my regular population, these women usually healed with no difficulty, and the exam would go smoothly. Awkward questions about future birth control would be asked and jokingly answered, as well as inquiries about their plan for future routine gynecologic care. I found that these women, above all in this situation, wanted honesty. Game playing and manipulation were hobbies (or careers) for another place and time.

Which brings me to telling you about my next patient.

Carla

I am guessing that any good medical drama worth its salt will show you how doctors and nurses grow hardened and cynical as they interact with and inevitably get taken advantage of by conniving masterminds. Although I generally avoid these shows, I can assure you that they are very likely *not* exaggerating. Just when I thought I'd seen it all, a new ruse would catch me off guard and send me into orbit, especially if it jeopardized my good name.

No matter what specialty I worked in, there were always, *always*, connivers, shysters, and con artists working to stir the pot. In my experience, I found that these people were bona fide geniuses, and I often wondered where they would be in the world if they had used their cunning in the pursuit of a higher calling. In the interest of brevity, I will limit myself to describing one representative case.

Carla, a thirty-four-year-old with a history of chronic kidney disease and fibromyalgia, immediately informed me during her initial appointment that she had severe back pain that had never been adequately controlled with anything other than Vicodin, and lots of it. Now, everyone knows that drug-seeking behaviors are a huge problem, with vast numbers of people facing unimaginable journeys into addiction and pain. This is a heartbreaking and frustrating conundrum for the person with the prescription pad in hand who is trying their best to do right by patients whom they will only see once. Good thing for me that I, as the clinic nurse practitioner, did not have prescriptive privilege beyond nonnarcotic medications.

"Carla, I can only imagine how bad your pain must be. Unfortunately, I can't give out anything stronger than ibuprofen, so you'll need to see your regular doctor to help you manage your pain postoperatively. I *will* say that ibuprofen really targets menstrual cramps better than almost anything else due to the way it works, and taking it regularly *before* you get cramps, along with a heating pad and hot drinks, will really help."

Carla shrugged and rolled her eyes. "You don't understand. I've tried it and nothing else works."

"I believe you. I am sure you know your own body," I offered, and continued to repeat that as she plied me with every imaginable trick in the book before stomping out of my office in anger and disgust.

A few days later, I got called into Marilyn's office.

"Patrice, did you call in a prescription to CVS under Dr. Goleman's name authorizing Vicodin for a patient?"

"Nooo," I groaned, certain of what she was about to say.

"Well, the pharmacy just called and said you authorized it."

I told her about Carla, and she wearily took notes to share

with the pharmacy and our legal counsel. Of course, I still got the lecture about being more careful, and even though I searched my brain for ways that this could've been avoided, I knew that it was probably inescapable in this particular case.

I'm given to understand that it's a lot harder nowadays to do this due to the measures put in place during the opioid crisis, and I am relieved. Through the years, I've seen copies of prescription blanks with my name and hard-earned credentials at the top and some really interesting medications and number of refills scrawled in an unfamiliar hand. I am very, very happy that I no longer have to deal with being a prescriber, having given up that aspect of my practice when I decided to teach full-time. From forgers to coworkers to friends pleading for a script for this or that, I never liked that aspect of being a nurse practitioner. Prescription privileges lead to all sorts of annoying situations, even if I was only able to prescribe medications that weren't particularly addictive. Every now and again I still get letters in the mail asking me to verify my signature on some very clearly illegitimate prescriptions. There sure are a lot of unscrupulous people out there.

Abby

My years of hospital experience never prepared me for the intimacy and weirdness of the clinic. If you are an outpatient provider of any sort, you know what I am talking about. Despite the many invasive and physically personal activities that are carried out in hospitals every day, there is an atmosphere of clinical briskness that seeps into every interaction inside those venerable if somewhat sterile walls. It's usually safe and very easy to keep one's professional boundaries, sometimes to the detriment of meaningful human interactions.

I carry that sense of boundaries with me whenever I shrug on a lab coat or a pair of scrubs, but every now and again an interloper oversteps into my zone. Enter Abby.

"Hi, Abigail, I'm Patrice, and I will be doing your exam today. How are you feeling?"

"Oh, please call me Abby. I am doing awesome! How about you?" Abby was a 31-year-old vivacious brunette with an easy smile. This was going to be quick and pleasant.

"I'm doing well, thanks. I'm going to do a quick exam to check and see that your uterus is coming back down to its pre-pregnancy size and that there are no signs of infection, okay?"

"Sure. No problem, Patrice!" she said as she easily slid down the exam table and put her feet in the stirrups.

I donned my gloves, gently inserted my fingers into her vagina, and palpated her abdomen using a bimanual approach, checking the shape and position of her uterus. "Everything feels really good. You're healing well," I said.

And this is the point where I pause when I'm retelling the story in class and ask my students what I did wrong. They will generally give me a quizzical look. Never does anyone guess what came next, but once I tell you, you will not forget the lesson either.

"Oh my god, I feel really good, huh? Patrice, are you flirting with me?"

I froze. With one gloved hand in her vagina and the other on top of her abdomen, I fought my urge to panic. Being a female provider, it had never occurred to me in the hundreds of exams that I had performed that I would've needed a medical assistant in the room as a witness.

Choking down bile, I calmly removed my hands and discarded my gloves. In my most professional tone, I told her that I meant that she was healing fine and could resume all of her normal activities, steadying my voice as best I could. I asked if she had any questions as I walked over to leave the door ajar after the exam for any further discussion.

She looked a little crestfallen that I hadn't taken the bait and gave me a "No, everything's cool," before I said goodbye and shut the door behind me, legs shaking.

"Patrice, what's wrong? You look like you just saw a ghost!" exclaimed Imelda, the medical assistant who was helping me that afternoon.

"*Oh. My. God.* Imelda, you *have* to come into the rest of the rooms with me today, okay?" I briefly described what had just happened, and she shook her head in disbelief. She knew the protocol that male providers always needed an escort, but she and the other busy assistants appreciated not always having to stop what they were doing every five minutes when there was a female provider on the schedule. She grudgingly agreed.

Later, I called a colleague to ask if this had ever happened to her, and if so, what I should do to prevent it in the future. She chuckled appreciatively and offered the following advice.

"Some of these girls are just plain crazy, aren't they? Flirting with you while they're on the table, for God's sake."

"Well, maybe she was flirting, *or* maybe she was getting ready to accuse me of molesting her!" I said in a cold sweat. "I documented the encounter briefly in my notes, but it's still my word against hers, isn't it?"

"Well, yeah, but I wouldn't worry about it. Weirdos try stuff all the time. Just flag her chart that she should never be seen alone if she ever comes in again."

So, the moral of the story, or the teaching pearl, as we like to call it, is to never, *ever*, under any circumstances, say that someone's body feels good. You just never know what people are bringing to (and onto) the table.

Darcy

Darcy was the kind of kid you might expect to see on any given day at an abortion clinic. Seventeen years old, first pregnancy, with large, soulful, kohl-rimmed brown eyes and a large chunk of metal partially occluding both nostrils. Spiky green tufts of hair peered out defiantly from under her gray woolen cap. I liked these kids.

She flumped down, fully dressed, onto the exam table and folded her arms. I quickly guessed that we were not going to be doing a pelvic exam today given that she had opted not to follow the instructions of the medical assistant who had brought her into the exam room and left her with a paper drape that was still folded neatly beneath her black denim bottom.

"So, Darcy, how are you feeling since the surgery?" I ventured.

"Fine."

Okay. For some reason, this young woman had chosen to show up, unlike the 60 percent of the rest of the patients from her surgery day, so it was my job to figure out why.

"Normally, I do a quick pelvic exam and then go over in-structions for things like routine gynecologic care and birth control. Have you ever had a pelvic exam before?" I asked.

"Well, obviously I *have*, or I wouldn't be here, right?" she replied evenly.

"I see that you were asleep for your procedure. Was that your first experience with a gynecologist?"

Darcy sized me up before her answer. "Yup. They made me splay my thighs onto these weird leg holder thingies and then clamped a mask over my face. It was a real fucking party."

Ah, got it. I think it's a crying shame that we sanitize and terrorize our young in such a way that they feel violated every step of the way. They are tough little marshmallows, these kids, coddled with the gift of being able to avoid visceral pain but left clueless and frustrated at being cheated of the genuine experience of being a human woman. Some brave or sadistic moms would insist on their daughters being awake during the abortion, but rarely was there one who did so with great love and tenderness so that her daughter would truly understand what was happening to her. Often, these were the ones who simply couldn't afford the anesthesia.

"If you'd like, I can do a mini exam while you're awake today so that you will get a taste of what a full annual exam is like. I can't do a Pap smear today since it would probably show some inflammation from the surgery, but I can walk you through the rest of it. It's up to you."

"Why do I need to go to a gynecologist every year anyway?"

"Well, it's useful to get checked for infections or cancer, and to get birth control."

"So, I can't get the pill if I don't go to a doctor and spread my legs every year?"

I didn't have the heart to tell her that plenty of providers, in addition to yearly exams, rope you into coming in and paying every six months for a blood pressure check in between, as the pill can elevate it. Not generally an issue with a 17-year-old, but there you have it. Yes, they charge for it, not necessarily out of greed but more often because—God forbid—that would be the one time that they would miss something and get sued.

"Well, I wouldn't put it like that, but yes. It's really not a bad idea to check in and talk to your doctor or nurse once in a while," I added.

"It sounds like a pretty shitty idea if you ask me, holding women hostage so they can get birth control even though they could easily come in and get tested for things on their own."

I found myself getting defensive at her words, which insinuated that those of us who work in women's health are just as controlling as the rest of society when it comes to disempowering women to make their own decisions about their bodies. In fact, I had recently been to a seminar that discussed the notion of making birth control pills over the counter. Darcy was right; there's very little reason why they shouldn't be. We know damn well that without our oversight, there'd be little reason to go in every six months just for a blood pressure check that they could easily do at home or while shopping at the drugstore.

I wish I could say that I burst out laughing and agreed with her, but I was still a pretty uptight believer in established protocols at that point in my career. I asked again if she would like to get the experience of a rather short and painless pelvic exam, and to my surprise, she sighed and agreed that she might as well. As with all my newbies, I did my best to talk her through it as I went, and she did just fine.

Corinne

The other end of the spectrum freaked me out quite a bit when I saw women who were hovering around age 50. To me, it seems so tragic that just as you are about to be free from the beautiful but seemingly endless obligations that come from raising a family, you can end up with that surprise change-of-life baby. I remember my grandmother saying that she relished it when she had my aunt at age 44 after having raised three other daughters, but my aunt herself told a different story of feeling unwanted and ignored as her mother pursued a long-awaited career as a receptionist in a doctor's office that had been postponed in order to be a homemaker.

Corrine was 49½ years old and had 3 kids. *She* had no idea that she should ever question the rules of the gynecologic exam game, and was ready and waiting, legs expertly splayed with her feet in the stirrups as I entered the room. Her perineum was the first thing I saw. I walked around to the side of the table to say hello and inquire how she was doing.

"I am doing great, super relieved that this is over and I didn't have to have another baby at my age!"

"Oh, wow, yes, I see that you would've been 50 if you had carried to term." I scanned her chart as we talked. She was relaxed and quite chatty as I examined her, a marked contrast from the tense monosyllabic teen that preceded her.

Not for the first time, I noticed the distinct differences between older and younger patients in both mind and body. Please don't get sad or insecure about what I am about to reveal. There is great beauty in women's bodies at each end of the life span. Men and women alike have been trained to revere the tight, pink membranes of youth with their hymens and slit-like cervical openings far more than the slackened and comfortably lubricated vaginal opening of a mature woman. Indeed, in many areas of Sub-Saharan Africa, it's a common practice to pack the vagina with drying herbs to keep it tight and dry to ensure the ongoing thrills of a vaginal deflowering during intercourse that transpired with an unblemished young woman who lacked any experience with which to compare this encounter.[46]

I always hid a secret smile when examining a seasoned mom, a woman whose relaxed body was open to envelop her world as she took in daddy, pushed out babies, and opened her bra to breastfeed a baby while sitting on the toilet refereeing kids in makeshift terrycloth loincloths as they chased each other in and out of the bathroom wielding toilet brush swords. I was that woman too. Even now as my family grows older, the feeling of being a semipermeable membrane, of home and family life flowing back and forth through my being, stays with me.

As I type this, my son drifts into my office to get my advice on contacting an insurance agent and the cat alternately howls and purrs to get my attention. I am not surprised at all as I recall busy moms interrupting my well-honed instructions in the exam room to answer their cell phones and yell at or cajole their needy families before they even had a chance to pull their feet out of the stirrups. What *did* surprise and sadden me was when I would walk into a room to find a woman asleep on the table. To be so exhausted that this was seen as a moment of respite astounds me to this day. Ever the givers in and of life, women's life lessons often include learning to set healthy boundaries as a gift to themselves and the beloved creatures they nurture. I've known more than one woman who has longed out loud for the day when she can take a crap in peace. The trick is, when that day comes, to let go of being needed.

And if a woman succeeds at a certain age, she is unstoppable. She can open herself and her aging body in ways that no alluring young virgin can. Smart lovers sense this. As virtually all confident, sexy older women know, it takes a highly evolved human to appreciate making love to a being that is so like a ripe, juicy peach in her sensual, embodied knowing. And when they do, their knees buckle in gratitude and deep homage to the person that this woman has survived to become. Her wisdom and sensuality know no bounds. So don't fret that your vagina isn't taut and your labia are a tad floppy. Just don't.

"You're good to go," I said to Corinne as I finished her exam. "If you don't get a normal period in four to eight weeks, don't panic, but do give us or your regular doctor a call. And don't waste your money on home pregnancy tests; they can be positive for quite a while after the abortion."

"Lemme tell you, they *better* not screw up my appointment to get my tubes tied again! I've had two appointments that got canceled. The first one was canceled due to their equipment breaking, and the second was during that huge snowstorm, remember that? I got pregnant waiting to reschedule!" Corinne grimaced in her frustration, then chuckled. "Oh, well, now off to the grocery store. I swear, my kids are eating me out of house and home!" Corinne sat up briskly, shimmied on her pants, and grabbed her cell phone, which had been dinging the whole time.

She cheerfully thanked me again for being there for her and went on her merry way.

As I drove home that night, after a jam-packed day of teaching followed by these evening follow-up visits, I reflected on the great privilege of having a bird's-eye view of women across their life spans. The myriad ways in which they see themselves and the world around them never cease to amaze me. From the pointed accusations of a clear-eyed teen to an older woman's cheerful acceptance of the rigid and sometimes ridiculous rules by which we in health care play the game, I can now sit back and honor it all for being what it is. How I could've done better, and if I even wanted to, was always another story, however.

Part Two

AS YOUR FAITHFUL SCRIBE, I have many more tales up my sleeve to tell about my life as an abortion clinic nurse, but for now I'd like to switch gears and do something a little different.

A while back, I watched some truly inspiring educational videos that contextualized how and why people find themselves sitting in front of someone wearing scrubs, a lab coat, or a stethoscope. The video was brilliant in that it allowed aspiring nurses to see the patient's point of view, when it is usually easy to make assumptions about them in our brief time together.

In the everyday hustle and bustle of our busy jobs, understandably, sometimes we simply have no time to delve into the deep intricacies of our patients' lives. We're so eager to do our jobs efficiently that it's easy to forget that every patient has a complex and interesting story far beyond a particular moment in our clinic. In truth, it's really not most people's favorite place to be, and it constitutes but a small fraction of their actual lives, which continue long after the doctor or nurse practitioner tears off a few prescriptions and sends them on their way.

With clinical experience, practitioners often grow numb as patients' stories repeat themselves in all kinds of iterations. They lose their punch, and we learn to whittle them down to the nitty-gritty to efficiently get to the topic at hand. But frankly, patients have a similar experience of us, right? I often reflect, sometimes wryly, how very little impact I have probably had in the grand scheme of someone's life. Just as with the carefully written postoperative instructions that I so often found in the discharge lounge trash can, I am reminded that the knowledge and skills that I offered were only a drop in the ocean of my patients' lives.

However, I have learned to pay attention for my own sake to prevent burnout. For *this* is what moves me deeper into my humanity. The touchy-feely stuff. To be sure, my attempts to creatively explore the context of various encounters would cause many of my sophisticated Ivy League students to offer scathing critiques. Students with expertise in philosophy or the arts might roll their eyes at my amateur attempt at reimagining the lived experiences of those we serve. But just as I advised them to suspend their critical eye for a moment, so too do I ask you to do the same and really just listen. People's stories, however humbly or ineptly communicated, are real.

Over the next few stories in Part II, I attempt to step into my patients' shoes and share fictionalized and reimagined accounts of their lives, each story inspired by what I encountered in reality. The following portrayals help us take a few steps back from the woefully sterile and impersonal clinic environment as we examine the intersection of the lives of most men and women who, like so many of us, spend very little time as patients in health centers.

And I promise to keep you company. Just like Alfred Hitchcock's cameos in his movies, I might pop in to say "hi" once in a while to remind you that I am still here.

SIXTEEN

Johanna And Jess

"Nothing is more difficult, and therefore more precious, than to be able to decide."

—**Napoleon Bonaparte,** *War Maxims*

SHE TOSSED HER KEYS hastily onto the wrought iron hook by the front door as she hurried in with her bags. Johanna blew her bangs out of her eyes (Why is this *Friends* hairstyle still popular? It drives her nuts!) as she set down two bags of groceries from Whole Foods and three bags from Crate and Barrel. She was pretty pumped when she peeped in to see the perfectly coordinated patio cushions. What a find!

She cradled her phone as she started to unpack the bags. "Hi, yeah, I get what you're saying; I just don't see why we can't go with the adjustable-rate mortgage...oh, yeah, that's true, if the rates go up, we could get screwed. Okay, we'll figure it out later." She walked into the kitchen with the groceries as 17-year-old Jessica sauntered in. Her daughter had always been a bit secretive, and lately all Johanna saw of her was a glimpse of her long legs and long blond hair. Jess started rummaging through the grocery bags (she'd been ravenous lately) and tore open a bag of organic blue corn tortilla chips, her favorite.

"Your prom dress finally got here! It looks really pretty. Let's see you try it on after dinner, okay?" Johanna swept through the kitchen unpacking and putting things away while simultaneously giving a quick wipe to any counter surface that harbored even the tiniest of coffee drips or crumbs. It was an unspoken and unappreciated talent she possessed.

"Um, yeah, well it'd better be quick because I am going out with Katie and Meghan, like, super early," was the reply from under the curtain of falling blond hair as Jess bent purposefully over the chip bag.

Dinner was the usual affair of setting out nicely prepared foods on the counter with everyone grabbing what they wanted. Honestly, all that crap about eating dinner together was the stuff of Boston Market commercials and *Parents* magazine advice columns. Juggling work, school, and sports schedules to accommodate a sit-down dinner even two nights a week seemed like a daunting, if not downright impossible, task.

Sitting on her daughter's bed later, Johanna surveyed Jessica with a practiced eye as she zipped up the back of the silvery, slinky dress. It was a little bit of a tight fit.

"Hmm, what do you think, honey? It's a little snug, but remember the one last year was too, and when we cut your carbs back it zipped right up!" Johanna laughed, remembering her daughter's hypoglycemic grumbling the week leading up to junior prom. She ruefully patted her own tummy and grew nostalgic over the time in her youth when she could do the same. Now it took friggin' 10 weeks of Weight Watchers and almost daily Zumba to drop even five pounds.

"Yeah, um, Mom? About that..."

Not two seconds into cramming some food into my mouth for much-needed sustenance, the phone rang. "Patrice? Sorry to bug you, but I need to see you in my office," Anna Maria said in her usually terse manner. As I approached the open door, I could see the problem. A very well-dressed mom-and-daughter team were arguing heatedly, or I should say, the mom was freaking out while waving a checkbook and the sullen teen stood, defiantly monosyllabic, with her arms folded over her chest.

"What seems to be the problem?" I asked, although I was pretty sure I knew. This scenario was fairly common.

"Well, as I was explaining to Mrs. Shapiro, we cannot do the procedure if the patient does not consent," Anna Maria tapped her pen impatiently on her desk.

"SHE IS ONLY SEVENTEEN AND SHE DOES CON-SENT!" Mrs. Shapiro eyed us wildly as she spat out the words between clenched teeth.

"Okay, I can see this is really tough. Mrs. Shapiro, I am guessing that the counselor reviewed the consent process with you earlier, and as per state regulations, your daughter is considered an emancipated minor due to her pregnancy. We cannot force her to have an abortion against her will."

"SHE HAS NO IDEA WHAT SHE WANTS! SHE

IS A CHILD!"

I turned to the daughter. "What's your name?"

"Jessica."

"What are your thoughts, Jessica?"

"I told my mom. I don't want to have an abortion." She continued to look down at the floor, arms folded.

"HAVE YOU LOST YOUR MIND?" Johanna paused and took a deep breath before continuing. "Listen, Jess, we've been through this a hundred times. You are graduating next month, and you've wanted to go to Ohio State since forever. Do you really want to throw that all away to have a baby by that kid you barely even know?!"

Hoo boy, another one of these...we'd been having a run of pretty blonds from the burbs who were venturing into the inner city to hook up with the local youth recently. I could think of no better way to piss off their socially adept suburban parents. Kudos, kids, you have definitely gotten their undivided attention. I looked at the desperate, perfectly coiffed mom and felt enormous sympathy for her plight. My own kids were still a little too young to stun me in this manner, but I felt a moment of panic at the thought of colicky babies and midnight diaper changes just as I was about to reclaim some freedom from relentless parenting.

I cleared my throat. "I am so very sorry, but it seems that you two are going to have to talk this over some more. Jessica has the right to make her own decision, and we cannot force anyone to do anything without their full consent." Johanna eyed me with icy loathing as she slammed down her purse on the counter, then picked it up again and tucked the checkbook angrily into it before storming down the hall. Jess flipped her pretty, highlighted hair out of her face, squared her tiny shoulders, and ambled down the hall after her mom.

I never saw them again. I think of them every once in a while, wondering how life turned out, and I'm optimistic that they have grown and changed in very interesting and unexpected ways.

SEVENTEEN

Melissa

"What are men to rocks and mountains?"

—Jane Austen, *Pride and Prejudice*

"OH GOOD *LORD*, CAN I leave now?" Melissa muttered to herself as she poured yet another round of cheap chardonnay into a small plastic wine glass. In the two years following her husband's death, this speed dating social that her sister-in-law had persuaded her to attend was by far the worst idea yet. The reception room was crowded and noisy as singles of all ages giggled and juggled appetizers and drinks, their name tags prominently displayed. Long tables with chairs on either side lined the far end of the room, complete with index cards, pens, and timers neatly organized for each. The evening festivities had already started, with men and women sitting facing each other across the tables, attentive and focused on the quick banter of the strangers they were assigned to flirt with for five-minute increments before moving on to the next person. A casual observer would easily note that this was rarely loads of fun for most participants, although some were clearly really adept at the game, sizing up candidates with the sharp eye of a college sports talent scout scrutinizing the high school hopefuls out on the football field for the fall lineup.

Melissa straightened her name tag nervously as she noticed it had sagged on her silky blouse and was now sitting squarely on her left boob. She sidled up to the corridor leading to the exit door when a young man approximately half her age held up his hand in a stop gesture and smiled.

"You're not leaving, are you?" He waved his drink toward the door and shrugged questioningly.

"Oh, um...well, my babysitter called and she said the kids are arguing pretty badly, so, um, yeah, I gotta go."

"Yeah, well, I don't blame you. If I had kids as an excuse, I would be outta here so fast."

Next thing you know, there she was, tangled in the cheap Ikea bedsheets of a seductively charming 23-year-old grad student, breathless from being way out of practice in the sex department. He returned from a short trip to the bathroom, all tousled and adorably skinny as he settled back into the single bed and stroked her exposed belly, tracing his finger with wonder over her C-section scar. Melissa grew self-conscious and gathered her things. She sheepishly grinned and thanked him for a fun night. Her boy lover sighed and walked her to the door before telling her that she had an amazing life-giving body. They exchanged numbers and she went out to her car.

I guess it would come as no surprise, since you're reading this book, that she missed her period that month and found herself pulling into the driveway of the women's center for her scheduled surgery seven weeks to the day after that awkward—though lovely—encounter with the sexy, hair-tousled boy in the Ikea sheets. She vaguely recalled some urgent ministrations with condoms during the blessed event, but clearly something had gone awry.

She was lucky to have scored an early appointment, knowing from experience that it was always best to be one of the first cases in an outpatient surgery clinic. As a receptionist and scheduler at a busy orthopedic practice, she often urged patients to get the first appointments in the morning before the snags and delays started happening and things got backed up as people showed up with incomplete paperwork, consents not signed, or missing lab work. The other perk in arriving early was that you were far more likely to see as few other patients as possible. This was a large suburban town, but you never knew who you might run into.

Melissa strode across the waiting room purposefully before pulling off her large sunglasses and signing in. She did a quick survey of the room and found a relatively quiet seat in the corner near the health information brochures. She sighed with relief as she looked around and saw that, as suspected, there were still a fair number of empty chairs. She froze in disbelief when she stole a glance at the young girl sitting two seats down. *OH GOD, PLEASE TELL ME THAT THIS IS NOT HAPPENING.* Melissa twisted in her seat and practically ran up to the front desk.

"Uh, excuse me, but I have a *big* problem," she said to Phyllis, the good-natured but tough-as-nails receptionist who took crap from no one. Phyllis looked up inquiringly over her half glasses. "I know that girl over there. She is on my daughter's field hockey team!" Melissa surreptitiously nodded at the teenager playing absentmindedly on her cell phone in the corner.

"I see. And what, exactly, do you want me to do about it?" Phyllis patiently put this back on the patient. She had seen and heard it all: two girls who were fighting over the same guy, husbands showing up with their girlfriends while their soon-to-be ex was there with a friend, cops who worked together, you name it. It was never pretty. Even more uncomfortable for Phyllis personally was when a neighbor or church acquaintance walked in and grew pale at the sight of her, but after eight years, she was pretty used to that by now.

"I don't know! Oh my god! I can't take more time off to reschedule, I just can't!" Melissa wailed as she sunk her head in her hands, tears of panic welling up.

"Okay, tell you what. We'll schedule you two as far apart as we can so you hopefully won't run into each other, but I can't guarantee anything."

Unable to think of any alternatives, Melissa slunk over to another corner of the waiting room, which was mercifully filling rapidly with other patients and their lively family members. She kept her head down, pretending to be immersed in a magazine until her name was finally called. She breathed a sigh of relief when she was whisked down a hall to a small ultrasound room, hopping up onto the exam table and quickly scooting down her jeans so the technician could place the transducer on her abdomen.

"Sorry, but we really need to use the vaginal probe for this. The pregnancy is so early we really can't get a good view any other way," the tech said kindly.

"Oh, okay. If you don't mind my asking, why do you need to do an ultrasound?" This seemed like a cruel and unnecessary indignity. Melissa had a flashback of much happier ultrasound moments when she had had her kids. She and her husband had looked forward to the moment when they would see that first little, fluttering heartbeat on the screen and listened eagerly as the ultrasound technician pointed out various body parts, fuzzy moving images on the screen that often looked very little like the anatomical structures being described. She had little inclination to want to see anything on that screen today as she shimmied off her jeans and panties under the paper drape.

"Well, it's important to properly locate the tissue, and sometimes women have what's known as a bicornuate, or double uterus. Wouldn't want to evacuate the wrong side, now would we?" the tech said cheerfully as she slid a condom over the probe head. Melissa meekly nodded as she scooched down and parted her legs.

Shortly after, she was escorted out and around the corner to wait her turn to see the counselor. As she was passing the cashier's office, she heard some yelling as a stylish woman ran smack into her as she rushed out angrily. The woman stopped briefly to apologize and drew her head back in surprise. "Melissa?"

FUUUCCKKK! "Oh, hey, Johanna, what a surprise," she managed to rasp out from her throat, which was now partially obstructed by her thumping heart. "Hi, Jess," she added weakly to the morose zombie behind her mom. "I...I'm so sorry to see you guys here."

"Yeah, well, this is certainly a fucking nightmare for all of us, isn't it?" Johanna gritted her teeth and decided to say no more.

This day could *not* get any worse. She then noticed that Melissa didn't have a daughter in tow and began to put two and two together. "Oh my god, this is just *awful!*"

"Um, yeah, I think we are sharing the worst day of our lives together," Melissa said as she grew a little dizzy and found herself inappropriately starting to giggle. "Listen. This sucks big time, I know, but your secret is safe with me, and I know we're all going to get through it somehow."

Jess found her voice and said flatly, "I'm not gonna go through with this. I don't give a shit what people think." Johanna's lips drew into a thin line as she grimly shouldered her purse.

"Well, see you guys later," Melissa offered feebly as they turned to leave. Johanna turned to give her a long, sympathetic, desperate look before she walked out of the clinic with her daughter, who was just as pregnant as when she had gone in.

Melissa fell limply into one of the infamous back hallway chairs and for the thousandth time in her life noted that being a woman was one of the most brutal things in the whole entire world. The level of secret cleanup that went on so that women could bravely continue marching themselves and their loved ones through to the next chapters of their lives was so very, very underestimated by even the most aware and sensitive of men. God help them if they ever had to endure any of this.

This thought persisted as she finally made it to the operating room after the counseling, medical exam, and cashier's office, all with agonizingly long waits in between on this typically busy Saturday. No fun at all, especially without being able to eat or even have a stinking ice chip. She followed the nurse into the cold OR in her peach gown and paper booties. Melissa had opted for local anesthesia, which the staff usually dissuaded women from if they had little experience, but with two vaginal deliveries and one C-section under her belt, it was a safe bet that this veteran could handle it.

The doctor came in and introduced himself. He was jolly and nonchalant as he explained what he was doing, first injecting a little lidocaine into the cervix the way a dentist numbs the gums before drilling a cavity. The dilation and evacuation were quick, and Melissa focused on breathing through the strong cramps that gripped her belly as the contents of her uterus were removed. She was complimented on her motionless stoicism, and that was that. The worst was over. She was wheeled into the recovery room and tended to by some of the kindest nurses she'd ever met, a husband-and-wife nursing team with all the patience of the Jewish angels that they were.

After a brief stint in the discharge lounge, getting some much-needed sustenance, Melissa was good to go. She breathed a sigh of relief when she saw her very best friend, Haley, pull up outside the exit door. Just as she settled in and clipped her seat belt, her phone buzzed. She saw with wry amusement a text from none other than the cutie-pie who had unknowingly contributed to this fiasco. He hadn't heard from her in a while and wanted to know if they could do coffee sometime? She tossed her phone back in her purse, leaned the seat back, and closed her eyes.

EIGHTEEN

Caitlyn

*"There is no greater agony than bearing an
untold story inside you."*

—Maya Angelou, *I Know Why the Caged Bird Sings*

HMM, IS IT POSSIBLE TO *buy pregnancy tests in bulk?* she wondered to herself as she threw yet another negative strip into the trash. Honestly, these disappointments were adding up big time! She often joked to her husband, Josh, that they should consider buying stock in e.p.t. since they alone contributed probably thousands of dollars to the company's profit margin. After almost three years of trying to get pregnant, she was starting to develop a wry sense of humor indeed.

Caitlyn pushed her long bangs out of her eyes, sat down on the bed, and cried. This was her monthly pity party, and she allowed herself the honor of feeling crappy and disappointed before she picked herself up again and resumed her normal activities of daily living. First line of business was to call her infer-

THE VIEW FROM THE CLINIC

tility doctor's office and let them know her results. Even though she could've waited until the next week to tell them during her appointment, they were always so nice and super sympathetic when she called, a welcome pat on the shoulder that she just couldn't request anymore from her closest family and friends who had given up inquiring a while ago. Aside from her mom, they did this out of respect for her privacy.

Oh, her mom…Rosalind Hall was a lovely woman, a nurse, in fact. People loved her warm, motherly ways and sympathetic manner. She'd raised four kids and had eagerly gone back to work as soon as the youngest was in high school, finally returning to the work she loved, which had been cut short when she got pregnant just three months out of nursing school. Back in the day, she explained, women couldn't work if it was known that they were married with kids. Even without kids, hospitals were less than keen to hire anyone who might get pregnant anytime soon, so—as recently as the 1960s and well into the seventies and even early eighties when women's lib became de rigueur—married women learned to settle down into their roles as full-time housewives and mothers.

It wasn't that Caitlyn's mom was not a great mom; far from it. She was the kind of mom who patiently drove her kids to every single sports practice or choir rehearsal throughout their childhoods; made them thoughtful, delicious meals; and always managed to offer words of wisdom whenever they were upset. So it really stung hearing her mom sarcastically joke to her friends about being doomed to only grandcats, never grandkids; she decided they needed to talk. When she finally plucked up the nerve to tell her mom that she was having difficulty conceiving, the following conversation ensued:

"Hey, Mom, it's me. I... I'm really upset and wanted to talk to you about something. Josh and I started infertility treatment a few months ago, and, well, nothing's happened yet."

"Oh, um, hmm..."

"Mom, did you hear me?"

"Yes," was the vaguely defensive response.

"Are you upset or something? Josh and I have been married for five years now, and we really feel like we're ready to be parents."

"Well, all I can say is that I never went through anything like *that*, that's for sure! Imagine what it's like to be pregnant all the time and have people look at you like you're some kind of slut."

"Mom, I am trying to tell you that I'm upset!"

"I am sure you are; I just can't really relate. I'm sorry, honey. And just so you know, I am not going to quit my job and babysit if you decide to go back to work when you do have kids. I did *my* time," she said. And so Caitlyn changed the subject to something more pleasant, then hung up, shaken by her mom's uncharacteristically insensitive reaction.

It wasn't until later that Caitlyn was calm enough to able to piece together the frustration and shame that her mom was clearly still stuck in from her own days as a young woman. She tried to imagine Rosalind's experience as a woman who had in no way been permitted to indulge her career aspirations along with child-rearing. As her belly bulged four times in the span of six years, her hopes of doing the work she loved evaporated a little more with each child she birthed. The notion of women working for any type of self-fulfillment, still wildly unpopular with many, was simply not an option when Caitlyn was growing up. All the same, she was hurt that her mom couldn't have at least tried to sympathize.

Amazingly, while this was most certainly the most hurtful reaction she had received when talking to others, it wasn't actually the dumbest. Anyone who has ever gone through infertility treatment can tell you that they have heard absolutely all of these sometimes well-meant and yet ridiculous comments:

"If you just relax, you'll get pregnant in no time!"

"My cousin's best friend's sister got pregnant just by eating more [fill in the blank]!"

"You need to do it at least two times a day!" (Good god! No pressure *there*!)

"Do it doggie style; that will get you pregnant for sure."

"Once you give up trying, you'll get pregnant."

"Oh well, if all else fails, you can just adopt, right?"

Far worse were the people who didn't know her well enough to inquire intrusively about why she and her husband didn't have kids. It was staggering how monumentally rude people could be. Caitlyn and Josh were at the age where nearly all of their friends had kids, and it was getting to the point where they were going to have to massively expand their social circle in order to avoid the many sidelong glances as they attended birthday parties and christenings, with only the boldest coming right out and asking with a wink when they'd be next.

For Caitlyn, and especially for Josh, they were still early on in their journey of infertility and were a long way from contemplating a lifetime of childlessness. A little over a year into their experience with an infertility specialist, they were far from giving up. There were plenty of therapies to try, and they were still in the midst of the highly unromantic rounds of oral fertility drugs, scheduled sex, and charting morning basal temperatures.

Caitlyn regularly commented that medical professionals were "up in her business" far more than her husband these days. And when he was, poor man, it was really more like executing a strategic playoff game touchdown than enjoying the sweet escape of sensual lovemaking. Caitlyn winced every time she thought of him dry rubbing himself to produce enough ejaculate for the specimen cup and then running the sample over to the doctor's office. She couldn't begin to imagine what the hell he had to conjure up as a fantasy to be able to climax in that fashion. He was a sweet and simple man, no joke.

And then, one day, a miracle occurred. The day before she was scheduled to go in for one of those hellacious hysterosalpingograms where she would have to splay her legs wide open as a team of specialists shot dye into her cervix and watched it travel through her fallopian tubes to see if there was a blockage, she got a call from the doctor's office.

"Hello? WHAT? Are you *sure*? Oh my god!" Caitlyn wept big fat tears of relief and disbelief as she sobbed and hung up the phone after promising to do follow-up blood work to make sure she was progressing okay. She sat down shaking as she absorbed the news. She was pregnant. She got herself together and headed over to Josh's office to tell him the news. He emerged with a panicked look on his face as he met her in the parking lot as instructed, then burst into tears when he saw her face. They held each other, rocking and hugging while a few passersby discreetly looked down at their phones as they passed this emotional tableau.

A few weeks passed and all was well. The fertility clinic had her come in every few days for blood work to monitor her serum HCG levels, which were to double every three days for the first six or seven weeks if all was going well. Caitlyn felt great. She had no nausea or vomiting and felt like she could eat everything that wasn't nailed down. As advised, she and Josh kept the good news to themselves since it was common knowledge that, unfortunately, 20 percent or more of all pregnancies end in miscarriage, especially in the first trimester.

It was a bittersweet day when she was formally discharged as a patient at the fertility clinic. The staff sent them off with quiet jubilation that they had been able to help this couple's dream come true and jokingly told them not to call them when the dirty diapers and 2:00 a.m. feedings made them want to change their minds. Caitlyn was referred to an excellent OB-GYN for ongoing care.

By week 14, Caitlyn and Josh felt it was pretty safe to tell everyone the good news. As expected, their friends and family were overflowing with love and excitement. She even started sporting some cute maternity tops even though she knew it was a bit early. To be fair, her waistbands *were* getting a little tight, and besides, it would only be a few more weeks until she would really start showing.

Thankfully, Josh was able to finagle his schedule so that he could go with Caitlyn to her ultrasound appointments. Because she had gone through infertility treatment, she was monitored fairly closely, especially to rule out a multiple pregnancy—a common occurrence on fertility drugs—which they did rule out fairly early. Just one precious fetus, and they couldn't help but be excited every time they saw that rhythmic flutter on the ul-trasound screen.

Then one day, it was gone.

I always dreaded the moment when I saw a patient enter my office wearing maternity clothes. It invariably meant that this was one patient who would not float through my infrequent but sought-after smooth routine days, and I wouldn't have a prayer of getting out on time.

Patient number seven: first pregnancy, 14 weeks and 3 days, fetal demise due to anencephaly, also known as an absence of adequate brain tissue. I looked up from the manila folder to the woman who sat down before me. Caitlyn was stoic even as her puffy eyes betrayed the prolonged crying she had obviously been doing prior to being here. The fact that she had gone through extensive infertility treatment was not known to me at that time. No matter, as it was always clear from the diagnosis and afore-mentioned maternity clothes that this was one pregnancy that had been very much anticipated.

I cleared my throat. "I see here that you were referred by Dr. Lee. She's an excellent doctor."

"Yes, she is," came the whispered reply.

"I am so very sorry for your loss."

"Thank you. I feel very out of place here." Caitlyn started to cry.

I reached for the tissues that I often needed in my line of work and handed her the box. This sucked; it sucked even more than usual, if that was possible for a nurse who had chosen to work in an abortion clinic. There was nothing sadder than seeing the hopeful ones sitting side by side with the ones who couldn't get rid of their pregnancy fast enough.

"I know, it's terrible. A lot of obstetricians refer their patients to us because we really are considered specialists at doing D+Es (dilation and evacuations)," I explained. "We'll take good care of you, but I truly do wish there was another way. I am so sorry that you have to go through this."

I squared my shoulders and focused on the job at hand. Caitlyn did the same, and we were able to move without hesitation through her otherwise unremarkable history and physical. When we got to the birth control questions, I paused.

"Um, has your doctor given you any specific recommendations about getting pregnant again?"

"I...we haven't gotten to talk about it yet. I guess she just wants me to get through one thing at a time."

"Yes, that makes complete sense." I hesitated a little. "I just need to let you know that you could become pregnant again right away, so while it may seem strange to think about using some kind of birth control for the next cycle or two, we often recommend it so your body can replenish itself a little and you can get a good head start with prenatal vitamins. It's weird, but I can't tell you how many times I've seen people's fertility sky-rocket once they've been pregnant. It's like the pump has finally been primed, so be careful! I know you want to give your baby the best chances possible to be healthy."

"No, I understand, that makes complete sense. I was taking the vitamins the whole time I did the infertility stuff, so I'll just keep taking them, I guess. Thank you." Caitlyn rose out of her seat to leave.

"Caitlyn, I just want to say that I wish you and your husband the very best. Infertility is really, really hard. I've been there. I know." I almost never disclosed anything about my personal life to my patients, but something inside me prompted me to say it, knowing that it was not for my benefit but for *hers*.

Caitlyn looked at me in surprise and asked shyly, "Do you have kids?"

"Yes. A girl and a boy." I looked her dead in the eye. My message was unmistakable. "I truly wish you the best of luck. Hang in there."

That the abortion clinic nurse practitioner could sit there and hold space for this grieving young woman was a gift that I am glad I was able to give in that brief moment in time. It could've gone much differently, and it often does, sad to say. I am grateful to remember this as I look back and think of the hundreds—if not thousands—of other times that I didn't stop to notice a certain situation or couldn't possibly know how to say the one thing that might have meant the world to someone.

For what we say matters. I rub my eyes, and though I cannot recall even a fraction of the many patients I've encountered, I truly hope that I didn't traumatize anyone with careless actions or words that sometimes arose during a difficult day. If I did, it is only through the grace of my own healing that I have learned to forgive myself and know that life's shortcomings are inevitable. No matter how principled we are in thinking that we'll always do what's best, days and years wear upon us, and it's often all we can do to keep our own heads above water.

Every now and again, my kids remind me of some offhand

remark I made when they were young and how they still remember it to this day. Just as with Caitlyn, I can still conjure the sting in the memory of my own mother's dismissal when I tried to confess to her my fear and vulnerability around infertility. Caitlyn, I felt certain, would learn one day with her own kids that mothers are often harried or just plain thoughtless, and that has to be good enough. For they, just as anyone of us in a position of immense power over vulnerable beings, can be so caught up in their own stories that they succeed—spectacularly sometimes—in wounding the ones they work so fiercely to protect from the cruel world around them.

NINETEEN

Jody and Akshay

Men have every right to be intimidated by the power of women, the gatekeepers of life's most powerful longing for itself.

—Patrice D'Amato

SHE WAS LATE. NOT one to panic needlessly, Jody methodically put the final touches on the big work project she had been immersed in for the last three weeks, happy to have completed the computerized learning CDs for first-year surgical residents that she'd been working on for almost a year. As a reference librarian at one of the most prestigious medical schools in the country, she was excited to be learning a new skill set that would enable her to help doctors apply themselves not only in scholarly pursuits but also via case studies that would help them be better clinicians at the bedside.

Looking back at her decision to pursue a graduate degree in library sciences instead of going to law school, she smiled. Eight years earlier, newly armed with a dual undergraduate degree in philosophy and women's studies, Jody had seen herself shipping off to law school with the goal of specializing in appellate law to defend people whose only wrongdoing was challenging the status quo. During her college years, she had taken a research job at a law firm and really loved the complexities and nuances of the work. However, as she went through her undergrad courses with so many frat boys and future divorce lawyers (she actually knew a girl who bragged that she was going to law school so that she would be able to wrangle a mean prenuptial agreement for herself one day), she decided that the last thing she wanted to do with the next three years of her life was to waste it with aspiring lawyers. Besides, amassing a lot more student debt was a real concern since she was footing the bill by herself. After her dad died, her mom barely had enough money to make ends meet, and Jody was determined not to put pressure on anyone but herself.

She snapped her laptop shut, slid it into its case, and heard her friend Mai call out to her as she stood up to go to the elevator.

"Hey, wanna do happy hour over at Ivan's? It's two-for-one night!"

"Aw, that sounds great, but I promised Akshay that I would help him paint his bathroom." She pinched her nose to indicate her distaste at having said "yes" before this better offer. Mai just laughed.

"Ooh, sounds like a sexy date night for sure! You are a far nicer girlfriend than I would *ever* be! Oh well, have fun spackling, and see you in the a.m." Mai flipped her impossibly glossy long, black hair over one shoulder and cheerily waved as she departed.

Jody sighed as her brain jerked her back to the errands she needed to run on her way home from work, not least of which was to pick up a pregnancy test at the drug store. She exited the cavernous, cool library onto the dusty city sidewalk in the scorching heat and humidity that no one ever got used to in the steamy, soupy air of an East Coast summer. Centering her book bag squarely over her left shoulder, she walked briskly down the sweltering, busy street filled with cheerful café umbrellas and brightly flowering planters. Her cell phone buzzed, and she dutifully fished it out of the bottom of her bag before it alerted her a second time.

"Hey, sorry, but I'm gonna be late. Still finishing up all my charts after a crazy day, so I'll text you when I'm done."

She texted back. "No worries, I'll get dinner started. See you soon! Don't forget to pick up a bottle of wine; sounds like you're gonna need it, haha!"

One fine April day a few months back, when she was working the reference desk in the medical library, she looked up to find a rail-thin, studious type with a thick shock of black, wavy hair and melty brown eyes, as well as a nervous, serious demeanor. Akshay was a super nice intern who had asked for her help in doing a literature search for an assigned presentation during his first general medicine rotation at the hospital. She always wondered how someone could be so painfully thin but have such thick, healthy tresses. This was always her cue to note that enviably slender genetic stock, not malnutrition, was at play. For men such as these, this generally boded well for them rounding out ever so beautifully as they aged.

"Can I help you?"

"Um, yeah, I need to do a lit search on scleroderma."

"Okay. What specifically do you want to research?"

"Oh, um, well, I haven't really homed in on exactly what I'm looking for." He smiled tentatively, worried that Jody would think him quite ill-prepared, which, in fact, she did.

Jody was very familiar with this kind of request—the vague topic needing to be narrowed down enough so that they had somewhere to begin without having to ferret through 256,000 hits of articles in their massive database on a general topic of interest. It reminded her of her babysitting days with overindulged toddlers: *Now, Joey, which toothbrush do you want to use tonight? Do you want the red one or the blue one? Okay, blue. The blue one with dinosaurs or the blue one with Thomas the Tank?*

Akshay flushed a little as she asked kindly, "What kind of assignment do you need this for? Maybe we can start there." He pulled out the paper guidelines and they reviewed them together, deciding to focus on the respiratory symptoms and management of the disease. (For the record, scleroderma is a devastating connective tissue disease that can affect different areas of the body.) Jody—while not being even remotely confident about the topic—knew how to help. The beauty of being a librarian is that it means you can satisfy boundless intellectual curiosity without actually needing to know anything about the subject matter, at least initially. Statutory law, neurosurgery, nuclear physics—they're all fair game. Jody loved this aspect of her job and felt that she could traverse the universe simply by helping other really smart people get to where they wanted to go.

As for Akshay, he gratefully accepted this very pretty, intelligent, patient young woman's help with one of the endless short essays that were required when studying medicine. While they often involved an overwhelmingly broad variety of topics, some of which were less than thrilling to him, scleroderma was one subject he was actually excited about exploring. That he got to do so with this confident, curly-haired young professional made it even more palatable.

They spent a pleasant few minutes hunting through the thicket of articles on the subject before Jody regretfully glanced at her watch. "Sorry, this is going to take a bit more than a few minutes, but if you want, you can schedule a time during open sessions with me and I can help you a little more, okay?"

Akshay jumped nervously. "Oh, I am so sorry, I understand completely! I don't want to hold you up. Okay, well, thanks and bye!" He looked at the line of people behind him and bolted out of the library with lightning speed. Jody figured that was the end of him, which was too bad, but oh well. As he scurried away, Akshay cursed himself for acting like a nervous jackrabbit. It wasn't the first time that he scolded himself for spending his whole life with his nose in a book instead of sharpening his social skills.

But in fact, Akshay did indeed sign up for a one-to-one session with Jody, and soon after, for the first time ever, he was in love. As for Jody, she was cautiously optimistic about this new relationship, having been burned big time a year before by a colleague who had wooed her tenderly then decided to move in a different direction when things got serious. She had seen this pattern repeat itself several times in her dating years: guy can't get enough of you, life is good, guy starts to get cold feet, guy cheats. Between good therapists and plenty of self-help books, she knew the wisdom of the day implied that she was simply attracting men who fulfilled her expectations of failure, but deep down, she knew that that was bull crap.

There was nothing wrong with being the kind of woman whom men saw as someone they could spend the rest of their lives with. She had never been particularly needy and rarely felt any sense of urgency to push for a commitment. If a guy got nervous, that was his problem. Still, it *was* heartbreaking to go through this again and again. Despite all of this, she sensed that something was different with Akshay. His earnestness and attentiveness had not waned in the several months that they'd been dating, which were good signs—but now it made this current situation all the more difficult.

And so it was with monumental dread that Jody let herself into Akshay's apartment, peed on the stick, and awaited her fate. During the longest five minutes of her life, she unpacked the groceries, chopped veggies for a salad, and set the table. One minute before her cell phone timer went off, she walked resolutely into the tiny bathroom. To her overwhelming relief, there was no second stripe visible next to the control line. She sat trembling on the toilet, waiting the full minute to make sure she wasn't celebrating prematurely. When the ripples ringtone on her phone sounded, she knew the coast was clear. Wobbly with relief, she splashed water on her face, fluffed her sweaty curls, and applied a little lip gloss. She heard the front door open and the familiar jangle of keys being dropped into a dish as Akshay entered his apartment. Glancing at that fateful stick just one more time, Jody grew sick with horror. A faint but distinct second stripe greeted her disbelieving eyes. Oh god, it was now positive!

"Hel-*lo*? Anybody home?" Akshay set down the discreet

brown paper bag containing not one but two bottles of wine since he wasn't sure if he should've gotten red or white. He continued toward the bedroom and, as he did, saw a very shaky Jody sitting dejectedly on the toilet, fully clothed. His physician instincts told him in no uncertain terms that this didn't bode well.

"Oh my god, are you okay?" He knelt down anxiously beside her. She was incredibly pale.

Jody gave a quick nod toward the sink. "See for yourself."

"Oh my god," he repeated, examining the stick.

"Yeah." Jody looked up and, to her surprise, underneath the shock and concern on her boyfriend's face, there was a glimmer of—what exactly was that—*joy*? Her heart somehow managed to pound even harder.

She burst into tears, and he gently pulled her off the toilet and led her to the bed, caressing her hair as he cradled her sobbing, shaking body. After a good long time, she spoke.

"I can't believe this. The test was negative when the time was up, but not two minutes later, it was positive!"

"That's really weird. I guess maybe you're just like, really early. When do you think it happened? I mean, like how many weeks do you think you might be?"

"Well, my period was due last week, so I guess it could've happened when we went to the mountains the other weekend. What was that, like four weeks ago?"

Akshay searched his memory banks to calculate the exact date of that wonderful weekend. They had been able to steal away and borrow a friend's cabin in the gorgeous mountains nearby. Hailing from Florida, he had never known that this region could be so beautiful, with mountains to the northwest and coastline to the east, each only a short drive away. He recalled, too, the frustration of running out of condoms and having to resort to the pull-out method. What kind of idiot only manages to bring two condoms for an entire weekend? And even if he *had* brought enough, he knew the odds were not good: about 85 percent effective for condoms and 78 percent for the pull-out method.

"This is *crazy*! I am so pissed I want to scream! I called my gynecologist for an appointment to get on the pill back in *May*! Why do they make you wait, like, three months before you can get an appointment?" Jody wailed. "It's not like you can take morning-after pills three times a week while you wait!"

"I know. Jody, I am so, so sorry," he said sincerely, holding her face between his hands and searching her eyes for forgiveness.

"Me too." She dropped her head to his chest, and they lay back on the bed together for a very long time.

First thing Monday morning, Jody stole into the break room and dialed her phone.

"Good morning. Maple Glen Women's Center. Can I help you?"

"Yes, um, good morning. I have a question for you. I took a pregnancy test on Friday and when the time was up, it was negative. But then not two minutes later, it was positive. What does that mean? Am I pregnant?"

The woman on the phone didn't miss a beat. This was clearly not a particularly unusual question. And, between you and me, she had gotten her share of unusual questions.

"Yes, that happens sometimes. It could mean a couple of things. Sometimes the test can turn positive even if you're not pregnant if the chemicals sit too long. It could also mean that you are too early in the pregnancy for it to pick up enough of the HCG hormone the way it's designed."

"So, what should I do?"

"Really, all you can do is wait and retest in a couple of days. When was your last normal menstrual period?" The phone counselor went through the typical list of questions and assured Jody that she would keep her information on file in case she wanted to schedule an appointment to discuss her options. Jody felt a wave of tension fall off her shoulders just knowing that there were people who were experts on this stuff. For the first time during this crisis, her body went limp with the exhaustion she had not been able to release until this point, knowing full well that it was only a brief respite.

She thought of poor Akshay and his confused but supportive state. "Hon, really, whatever you want to do, I support you 100 percent," he said over and over again as they talked endlessly during the next few agonizing days. And she knew that he truly meant it. Her week dragged as she searched herself desperately for some kind of sign that she was or was not pregnant. She felt the same way she always did just before her period: sore breasts; nagging, sinking cramps deep in her abdomen; and the usual junk food cravings. When she queried a couple of her friends who had kids, they all told her that they had felt this way too when they discovered that they were pregnant. "It's like your period wants to come but it just never does," was how one aptly put it.

Mai noticed that something was up. By Thursday, she approached Jody and asked her out to happy hour again. Jody gratefully took her up on her offer.

"So, what's going on, my friend?"

"Oh Mai, I'm sorry I haven't been myself this week. I have been so upset I just couldn't talk about it! I think I'm pregnant," Jody blurted out as they barely got settled into their seats.

"Ooooh, shit," Mai whistled between pursed lips.

"I *know*, right?! What the fuck am I supposed to do?"

"I guess Akshay knows, right? How is he?"

"Yeah, I told him right away. He is friggin' wonderful. He says it's totally my decision, and honest to God, I think he would be cool either way. To tell you the truth, I think he was kind of *excited* in a weird sort of way!"

Mai laughed the tiniest bit. "Oh yeah, guys are always so relieved when they find out that their fishies can swim upstream. I think it's some kind of primal thing. But it's really good to know that he is so supportive. Thank God!" She paused abruptly before asking, "Oh man, what're you gonna do?"

"I have no clue! Mai, I've never even met his parents! He met my mom a couple of times, and she'd be happy for us if we decided to have a baby, but from what I hear, his parents are super traditional. And *Catholic*," she added. "He sorta told them he was dating someone, but they don't know much more than that. For all they know, I am some nice Indian girl from Bangalore. And *pregnant*?! Oh my god!" Jody stifled a wail into her nearby cocktail napkin before taking a sip of her virgin margarita. How ironic *that* had sounded when she ordered it.

"Oh honey, this is *bad*. My parents would freak out about me dating a White dude even if I wasn't preggers, especially if he wasn't even Catholic!"

"I know," Jody sighed. "How is it that every single person

in my current circle of friends was raised Catholic except me?" She ticked off her fingers. "You're Vietnamese, Akshay is Indian, Addie is from Nigeria, and Rima's from *Syria*, for God's sake. How is being Catholic there even a thing?" (Turns out about 10 percent of all Syrians are Christian, with a majority of those being Catholic.) Although Jody's dad was Jewish, he had always declared himself a devout atheist, and while her mom had grown up Methodist, she also did not ascribe to any particular religion, preferring to emphasize raising their daughter to think for herself and strive, first and foremost, to be a good person.

"So, what are you going to do?" Mai repeated the question as she took a slow sip of her Long Island iced tea.

"I've decided I am not ready to have a baby. I'll repeat the test like they said, and if I'm really pregnant, I think I will go ahead and schedule an abortion." Jody faltered over her words, which sounded much more confident than she felt. In truth, she was deeply conflicted. She had every logical reason to terminate a pregnancy, and yet she felt a deep, irrational desire to be a mom, especially when she thought of Akshay's face when she had told him that she might be pregnant. For quite possibly the first time in her life, she felt unconditional love and support from a man that went beyond what he might have wanted for himself.

Mai's face softened as she grabbed her friend's hand across the table. "Listen, I am here for you. If you wanna call me anytime, day or night, do it! I can't believe this is happening, let alone to you, of all people! You're the most responsible, self-sufficient person I know, and whatever happens, I know you're going to be okay." They shared a big hug.

Later, Jody reflected on Mai's words as she sat on the subway on her way home. As she slumped down in her seat, two teenage girls plunked down in the seats in front of her, earrings the size of bagels dangling from their drooping lobes. In their skin-tight leggings and off-the-shoulder sparkly tops, they talked loudly enough for everyone to hear as they jabbered endlessly to each other and also to their phones.

"I was like, *whut*? Who you accusin' of stealing your boyfriend? I got pregnant by him long before you came along, bitch!"

"Oh my *god*, that's right, you sure were!"

"Anyway, he promised me he would marry me if I got pregnant, so who should be pissed, me or her?"

"He shoulda married you like he promised. Instead, he goes foolin' around with that bimbo."

"I *know*! He used to be pretty good about taking the baby sometimes, but I told him I don't want my son around her—*no time*! She evil, and I don't trust her."

The girls continued on with their chat, and Jody couldn't help but be mesmerized. It hit her right between the eyes that maybe, just maybe, there was a part of her that wasn't so different at all from girl number one. For if she was being totally honest with herself, she acknowledged that a tiny part of her had hoped for the delighted reaction she had gotten from Akshay. Had she also wanted to test her man to see if he would be true to his word? During their intense and beautiful lovemaking, she could not deny that there was a part of her that often wanted to sing out, "No, no condom, and please, *please*, come inside me!" She always felt a twinge of frustration when he would pull out at the last minute, pinching himself off and turning away.

Jody was thoughtful the entire ride, and when she got home,

she was startled to see a brownish-red stain on her panties. She cleaned herself up, tucked a thick maxi pad in her underwear, and went to bed with a heating pad. By morning, the bleeding was heavy, bright crimson clots soaking the maxi pad. Thankfully, this was now a choice she didn't have to make.

Akshay lay in his bed the next morning, using those first few moments upon waking to let his emotions play with him ever so briefly before meeting the onslaught of the day. He reflected that, beyond a doubt, he was a mere servant to the whims of nature, with life and death being forces beyond his control no matter how skilled a doctor he would ever become. For to love a woman also meant to love life and surrender his will to the power that pulsated through her life-giving body.

He could no more ask Jody to choose against her will than he could ask her to jump out of a plane. He truly would wrap himself around any path that she chose for their future. Despite the years of cultural programming that had told him again and again that men are superior to women in pretty much every way, Akshay was beginning to understand just how deeply a man could be pulled into the depths of his soul through his love for a woman. He also knew that as much as men swaggered and crowed, anyone worth his salt realized sooner or later that it was a rare man indeed who had even the slightest control over a woman's body or, most especially, her mind.

His phone rang. He jerked up in bed to lean over and answer it when he saw that it was Jody.

"Hey! Are you okay? Is everything alright?"

"Um, yeah... I'm bleeding. A lot."

"I'll be right over. I love you."

Jody was quietly sobbing on the other end. "I love you too."

TWENTY

Summer Sports

"Play is often talked about as if it were a relief from serious learning. But for children, play is serious learning. Play is really the work of childhood."

—Mr. Rogers, *You Are Special*

"SO, DID EVERYONE GET back to you? Did we settle for sure on the weekend of the 18th? I am *so* psyched, but I need to firm up the date to be sure that Mom can babysit." Lauren paid the check as Amanda left the tip on the table before they left the café. Hard to say who loved their Tuesday morning coffee ritual more, with both regularly declaring it the critical link to their sanity. Second only to this was their annual September girls' weekend getaway when the kids were all back in school after the never-ending summer vacation.

"Genevieve says she's in. I'm just waiting on Emily." Lauren distractedly texted on her phone as they walked to their mom-mobiles, sleek and roomy SUVs designed with busy families or glamping survivalists in mind.

"Lauren, we haven't heard from Emily in years! I say we just firm up the date, and if she surprises us by showing up, that'll be the best we can hope for," Amanda said in frustration.

"All right. I'll text Genevieve, and hopefully we can convince her parents that we won't trash the place like we did 25 years ago," Lauren chuckled.

"Speak for yourself! I was a mere waif along for the ride!" said Amanda indignantly, and it was true. As Lauren's younger sister, she had been a bookish and timid 16-year-old homebody when they lived at the beach that fine summer. Lauren still could not fathom what had made Amanda decide to come live with her and two other girls she barely knew. Maybe the prospect of the long boring summer alone with their parents had been enough to propel her to the edge of her comfort zone. Whatever the reason, what had ensued certainly did the job. And while she hadn't been too skilled at pitching in with housework, Amanda made up for it by being the diligent home security guard and reluctant housekeeper while the others came and went. She took her job as the Fun Police very seriously, wringing her hands in worry every time a new escapade unfolded.

September 18th came, and with it four women with overnight bags chattered and tumbled into the cramped little bungalow-annex in the heart of their favorite seaside resort. The fourth woman was Camille, who at 22 was not only the baby of the group but also Genevieve's daughter. She'd decided at the last minute to fill in for the absent Emily, who had never answered Lauren's texts.

"Oh my god! It hasn't changed a bit!" Lauren said as they

crowded around the tiny kitchen and living room before heading into the minuscule bedroom that housed twin beds and a small chest of drawers.

"Are there still snails on the shower curtain?" demanded Amanda. Three of the four women grimaced at this fine memory while Lauren dutifully went in and checked before informing everyone that the coast was clear. The teensy bathroom was clearly the one room that had been upgraded with a real shower stall that no longer openly communicated with the ground below through wooden slats—as was still typical in most outdoor shower rooms at the beach. Lauren recalled how she had recently gone to a designer-home open house and seen the most astonishingly stylish open floor plan of a bathroom with just a drain in the middle of the floor. The designer had noted it reminded him of his days as a child taking delicious, cold showers after a sunburned day at the beach. She supposed that maybe *his* fond memories included a vinyl shower curtain that had been sprayed faithfully with Lysol daily to keep the snails and slugs at bay.

"Was it really that bad?" Camille asked.

"Oh, it was *gross*! You'd be standing there buck naked, shampooing your hair, and the next thing you knew, after rinsing, you'd open your eyes to five slimy slugs staring at you from the bottom of the shower curtain!" Genevieve laughed as she recalled one of their favorite stories.

"I can see I'm in for some fun walks down memory lane this weekend," said Camille. In truth, she didn't mind. She rarely got to spend time relaxing with her mom, and it was fun to see her laugh. After two divorces, Genevieve worked several jobs while raising her kids as a single mom.

"Hell *yeah*!" Lauren cheered as she set out four plastic cups and poured each of them a generous glass of chardonnay. "Cheers to our childish youth! What a summer that was!" With that, everyone clinked their cups and settled in to reminisce.

Lauren recalled how nervous and lonely she had felt that summer when, as an almost 19-year-old woman of the world with one year of college under her belt, she took the bus down to one of the farthest points south on the state beaches, looking for a job and a place to live for the season. Her college dorm mate, Genevieve, a local, assured her that it would be no problem to find something quickly, and true to her word, Lauren easily found a room to rent. She hated it immensely; living in an old Victorian house and renting from a woman who clearly didn't want her there was not what she had envisioned when planning her summer break.

After a few horrible weeks eating ramen and wandering aimlessly, she finally landed a job as a kitchen helper at a local seafood restaurant, the kind where a plastic swordfish hung precariously along with fake starfish and crabs on fraying rope nets outside the main door. Lauren would sweat her ass off in the kitchen with the swearing cooks while servers hustled frantically in and out in black aprons, expertly balancing enormous platters heaped with fresh seafood and presenting them to newly tanned or sometimes deeply sunburned families—the dads of which always wore a white belt and matching New Balance sneakers.

Her luck began to change when she met Emily, a sweetly cheerful, giddy, ruddy-cheeked girl from out of state who had also come to live at the beach that summer. Both in desperate need of companionship and fun, they conspired to put their pennies together to find a place to live. As luck would have it, Genevieve was thrilled to tell them at the 11th hour that the tenant agreement for her parents' little rental unit annexed to their family bungalow had recently fallen through and they could stay there. Still a little strapped for cash in their new minimum-wage jobs, they were able to convince Lauren's little sister and Genevieve herself to share the space (and the rent) with them. Despite the fact that it was supposed to be limited to only two occupants, they crammed in and convinced Mr. and Mrs. Bouchard that they would be as discreet as mice, or as discreet as four bustling and fun-loving working girls could be at the height of summer.

In deciding who got to sleep where, Genevieve was the obvious choice to be selected for one of the twin beds in the bedroom. This was a no-brainer. As the oldest of the group who was also kind enough to pay rent in her parents' apartment, she clearly pulled rank. In retrospect, it ended up being kind of a poor choice since, out of all of them, she was the least likely to be sleeping in her own bed on any given night. Emily, the naive and eager stranger from the North, happily accepted the other twin bed as sisters Lauren and Amanda offered to share the daybed wedged in next to the front door; its trundle-style pullout almost completely blocked the door from the inside. Poor Amanda, a light sleeper, often got a jolt as someone invariably bumped into her cot at three in the morning.

The girls quickly established a routine that they all learned to live with for the next two months. Amanda and Emily landed jobs at Tiffany's Treasure Trove, a hopelessly tasteless tourist shop that specialized in elaborate shell lamps, personalized seahorse mugs, and a Pick Your Own Pearl station that allowed customers to plunge their arms into a fish tank to pluck out an oyster that was guaranteed to contain a pearl. The pretty salesgirls would then set these treasures into necklaces, rings, or earrings, much to the delighted gasps of their customers who marveled and snapped photos of themselves engaging in such crazy capers. Lauren continued slinging salads and seafood while Genevieve entertained all of them with her antics working three jobs as a waitress, EMT, and fudge counter girl at the legendary Cupid's Candies on the boardwalk.

No one knew how on Earth she managed to juggle her jobs along with about eight guys that summer, for Genevieve was a girl like no other; with her flashing green eyes and ample hips and thighs, she drove men wild. A women's studies major, she defied all stereotypes of what girls should do, say, and look like in order to snag a man. Lauren, looking down at her own size-two body, often mused about how ironic it was that while she was the one who was frequently complimented for her cute figure and manner of speech, it was Genevieve, big fertility goddess personified, who was always getting the dates.

For Lauren, while hot guys may have stared (or, in one case, dropped a refrigerator they were moving as she passed on the opposite sidewalk), they rarely were bold enough to ask her out. Quite honestly, women were more likely to approach her with questions. One day, as she walked down the boardwalk in a T-shirt and shorts on her way to work, a woman and her daughter approached and asked, "Excuse us for being so forward, but we've been watching you and are dying to know what we can do to get a body like *yours*?" Many years and two C-sections later, Lauren could've honestly told the woman that it had been merely the blessing of youth, not endless crunches, but she didn't know that at the time, so she just smiled encouragingly and said she really didn't do anything out of the ordinary. *If it's guys you want, better pack some more weight on those butts and bellies*, was what she mused to herself as she thought of her full-figured, seductive friend.

In terms of dating, the other girls lagged far behind Genevieve, with Emily preferring to hang out with a few girls she'd met at the tourist shop and Amanda staying home to enjoy innocent banter with Genevieve's numerous gentlemen callers. As for Lauren, she not only enjoyed two dollars more an hour in her sweaty kitchen job than her glowingly clean roommates who delicately teased pearls out of oysters, but she also had the advantage of being the only girl working amid the chaos and cussing of hardworking young men.

It would have been a bald-faced lie to say that Lauren ever denied enjoying the attention she got as she tromped around the kitchen in her grubby sneakers while the guys flirted with her mercilessly. In fact, she had chosen to start dating one of the line cooks who mentored her, partly out of attraction but also partly as a shield against unwanted advances. She learned soon enough that there was a fine line between good-natured fun and all-out abuse. For while she was well liked and valued as a hard worker, there were times when the line cooks, dishwashers, and even the owner went too far. Their incessant sexual innuendos combined with repeatedly sending her into the walk-in freezer so she would have good, hard nipples when she emerged were not her ideas of good-natured fun.

Slightly more amusing was the moment when a cook asked Tyler—an adorable, preppy college boy they had hired for the summer—to hand him a pack of buns, and Tyler gamely scooped Lauren up and lifted her over the metal workstation to the hearty laughs of everyone there. Her boyfriend, Mike, went along with it but Lauren knew that he would help draw the line if needed. When it got out of hand or downright lewd, Lauren did her best to make sure that—at least most of the time—she could be seen as a person who merited respect in her own right.

Ironically, although Lauren was awash in the smell of stale fried food when she got home each night, there was precious little by way of nourishment in their own little refrigerator. Truth be told, she was so sick of the smell that she often forgot to ask if she could take something home to her famished roommates, which caused Amanda and Emily to regularly show up at the back door of the restaurant like hungry stray kittens in floral sundresses hoping for a bite of some delicious table scraps. Often, all they could manage to do with their meager wages was pay the rent, so food was scarce.

Genevieve, despite being a crazed workaholic and dating machine, was actually much more thoughtful, and they could always count on her to fill the huge mixing bowl to the brim with scraps of fudge in every flavor, from the classic chocolate walnut to screaming-green marshmallow pistachio. Everyone vowed, from that moment forward, they never wanted to see that much fudge in one place again—especially as the only hangover food on hand.

Every now and again, one of the girls would go into a fit of domesticity and buy a few groceries. Although everyone made an effort early on, as time progressed it became clear that while Genevieve and Lauren were the ones most likely to buy provisions, it was tiny Emily who inhaled all the food. That girl was a veritable locust when it came to the sporadic meals they tried to scare up in the impossibly small kitchen. It was a growing problem, and Emily herself frequently apologized for being so ravenous all the time.

Genevieve the Bold was finally the one to tackle the issue head-on. "Em, what gives? I just bought twenty-five dollars' worth of food two days ago, and it's *gone*!"

"I don't know!" Emily wailed as she flopped down dejectedly on the daybed. "I just can't seem to stop eating! I am starving all the *time*! What's wrong with me?" Tears of shame sprang up into her pretty blue eyes.

Genevieve peered at her closely and paused just a moment before asking her, "Not to scare you or anything, but when was your last period?"

"Oh, well, it might be a little late, but I haven't done anything, so I guess it's just off a little."

"Is there any chance you could've been in a situation that you may not remember?" They all knew that Emily could certainly tie one on like the best of them when she was out drinking with her girlfriends.

"Um, well, I was at a graduation party back at home before I came here, and I remember waking up in the house of some weird guy I didn't know…" Her eyes widened as she slowly finished. "And, oh my *god*, I woke up and my underpants were lying on the floor next to me." She started to cry. "Do you think something…happened?"

Lauren, Genevieve, and Amanda grew quiet and tried to find a spot on the floor to focus on while a crescendo of panic rose in the room. Emily looked from face to face and screamed, "THIS CANNOT BE HAPPENING! TELL ME THIS ISN'T HAPPENING! I've never done it before, I am a *virgin*! You've got to believe me!" Not knowing Emily very well at all, the girls didn't know what to think, but her genuine agony was heartbreaking. They had all been warned about date-rape drugs being slipped into girls' drinks at parties, and it seemed very plausible that Emily, with her small-town naivete, could've been an easy target.

A few gut-wrenching days followed after Emily got up the courage to do a pregnancy test and had a positive result. As she struggled to think about her friend's options, Lauren grew pensive. She herself had been mightily relieved when she'd gotten her own period a few days earlier after a little scare involving a defective condom while having sex with Mike. He had made her a fantastic meal a few weeks before at his modest little apartment, and she never regretted for a moment savoring her very first bouillabaisse and orgasm on the same magical night.

She learned a powerful lesson that summer: for her, sex and food went hand in hand. She vowed that from that moment forward, she would always date a man who could cook. And for the most part she did, even going so far as to later marry a sweet and thoughtful professionally trained chef. This was, she believed, the most brilliant thing she ever did in terms of following her personal bliss.

"Oh my god, those were the days!" Genevieve sighed as she remembered her many conquests all those years ago. "Do you guys remember that guy Bob from Boston?"

"No…wait, was he the guy who stalked you everywhere and scared the shit out of me when I found him lurking in our bushes?" Amanda slung back her chardonnay with uncharacteristic abandon.

"Yup," grinned Genevieve. "I finally had to pay his bus fare after I shoved his sorry ass into my car and dropped him off on the interstate." Everyone giggled uncontrollably.

"Okay, ladies, can we please get back to the story at hand? What happened to Emily?" asked Camille, who'd been taking in every word. This story could easily have been about one of her friends, though at least now girls knew the critical importance of watching each others' drinks like a hawk at parties at all times. Still, even though this was common knowledge, there could be enough distractions that they might miss something.

"Oh god, this is the part that I *do not* want to tell," Lauren groaned as she set her glass down. She turned to her sister and added somberly, "I don't think *you* even know this part. It was definitely not my proudest moment." Amanda stared back in surprise, sure that she had known almost everything about that fateful summer. How on Earth could Lauren have contributed to this sordid mess?

"Emily finally opted to get an abortion, even though she had no idea how she was going to pay for it," Lauren explained. "Try as we might, even though we pooled all of our resources to help her cover the expense, we were still two hundred dollars short. And every week that Emily waited, the cost of having an abortion was getting higher.

"Then one afternoon at the beach, Genevieve casually mentioned that maybe my boyfriend could help. I was in a pretty foul mood about him since I'd just heard a rumor that he'd been seen hanging out with his former girlfriend…"

"For fuck's sake, Genevieve, why the hell would I ask *Mike* to help out?'"

"Well, he did screw you over, so he owes you."

"Yeah, but lucky for me I wasn't the one who got pregnant!"

"True, but that was pure luck, wasn't it? I mean, Emily really needs the money, and you *know* he has it! How would he know if you were lying about who's actually pregnant?"

"I can't do that! Even if I could, there's no way I could pull it off!"

"Okay, okay, just thought I'd mention it." Genevieve dropped the subject, flipping over onto her stomach to even out her impossibly dark tan. Not surprisingly, the conversation was abruptly interrupted by some Canadian guy who offered to rub lotion on her back.

Lauren had tossed and turned that night in a cold sweat, her 19-year-old mind pondering the direness of the situation. Emily was desperate. Mike was a total jerk—yeah, but that was beside the point. But was it? And let's face it, Genevieve had been the most generous of them all, offering up two hundred bucks of her own money to help, while Lauren had only pitched in seventy-five and Amanda could only scare up fifty bucks. Lauren cursed herself for being so stingy and fainthearted at someone else's predicament. She thought of Genevieve and her badass bloodline of strong women. For God's sake, the girl's great-grandmother had been a *spy* for the French Resistance in World War II! Wearily, she smacked her pillow and rolled over to sleep.

The next afternoon at work, Lauren sidled over to Mike and asked him if he had a minute. Wiping his hands on his sauce-stained apron, he followed her outside.

"Yeah, um, I heard a rumor that you are hanging out with Ashley again."

"Well, we are friends. Is there anything wrong with that?"

"No, it's just that I feel like things have changed between us. We haven't seen each other outside of work for, like, two weeks!"

"Look, Lauren, I've been really busy, okay? I'm sorry if I haven't had time to do stuff together."

She cast her eyes downward. "Yeah, well, I'm late. I thought you should know."

"Wait, *what*?! Are you kidding me?"

"No. I did a pregnancy test, and it's positive," Lauren bit her lip and a few tears welled up in her eyes as she thought about the big fat lie she was telling. She thought of Emily.

Mike stood speechless, rooted to the spot. He searched Lauren's face and found little to convince him one way or the other.

"Don't worry, I'm gonna have an abortion. I just need to save up two hundred dollars more, and I'll have enough to get the surgery."

Mike swallowed hard and worked his jaw. "Don't be ridiculous. I will help you with the money part."

"Right. Thanks. Let me know when you get the cash. It's

gotta be soon." Lauren quickly turned away and strode back into the kitchen to finish breading the flounder for the night's entrée.

A man of his word, at least in this situation, Mike handed over the crisp green bills the following day. Lauren had little difficulty feigning nausea during the transaction. This was, by far, the most deceptive and devious thing she had ever done. In order to both assuage her guilt and give credence to her lie, she went all in to support Emily and stayed glued to her side through the whole experience as if *she* were the one having the abortion. She even insisted on going out on a limb to try to speak to the doctor before the surgery. Back in high school, she had learned a few things about abortion from some people who had come to speak to her class, and she had a couple of questions.

Emily, who as it turned out had gone to Catholic school and thus had absolutely no information on what to do, was overwhelmingly grateful for the support. She and Lauren traveled back up the interstate and met with none other than Dr. Julius Stine, the nastiest and shadiest doctor that your esteemed author has ever had the dubious privilege to work with.

He tried to brush past them in the hallway, but Lauren jumped up and followed after him, eyes ablaze. "Excuse me, doctor, but I have a few questions about the procedure." He kept walking but slowed down as a few dozen startled eyes of the patients waiting in their chairs followed his face intently to see what he would do next. *Dammit.* Normally he could slink into the OR from the side door, but that day he had needed to meet with the administrator to voice his displeasure about recent billing errors. This day was really pissing him off.

"What is it?" he growled.

"Is it likely that my friend will have trouble having kids later?"

"Who told you that?"

"Well, I heard it in one of my sex-ed classes in high school." Lauren's voice faltered a little as her newfound courage was giving way.

"Let me ask *you* something. Have you gone to medical school?" Dr. Stine sneered down his nose at this rapidly withering little upstart.

"No, but—"

"Well, I have, doll face. If you can't get your head around any of this, maybe you should just go home." With that, he kept on walking.

Lauren waited for Emily after the procedure and drove her back to their little cottage in Genevieve's car. In the days and weeks that followed, she remained overly attentive but was pretty sure she failed to convince everyone at work of the lie that she had been pregnant and had gotten an abortion. She was a lousy actress, and since nearly everyone there had been through the abortion experience themselves, either as a patient or a partner, her secondhand account of Emily's experience, while accurate, was not entirely believable.

The women all gazed thoughtfully into their nearly empty glasses as they sat on the deck enjoying the last remaining moments of daylight. Amanda was the first one to speak.

"Wow, Lauren, you're right, I didn't know that you went ahead with the lie."

"Yeah, I'm a real Girl Scout, I know," Lauren murmured. "The good news is that I saw Mike a few years later and we actually went out and had drinks. I apologized profusely, and he just laughed and said I was a terrible liar and he figured I was just squeezing money out of him because he had been such a shithead. Which he was," she added.

"Well, I, for one, am impressed that all of you were so supportive," said Camille. "How's Emily, these days, anyway? I never hear any of you talk about her much."

"Actually, it's been a while since any of us has heard from her. She keeps a low profile. I guess she's still kind of embarrassed about what happened. I know I would be." Lauren helped herself to the last of the chardonnay.

"She's a second-grade school teacher back in her home town. For a few years she sent me little bits of money to try to pay me back, but then she stopped." Genevieve shrugged. "I feel bad that she feels ashamed. It would be really fun to see her."

Camille sat up, eyes blazing. "Why should she be embarrassed? If anything, she was the *victim*! I know this happened a long time ago, but this pisses me the fuck *off*!"

Lauren rubbed her forehead, Amanda picked at the lint on her sweater, and Genevieve heaved a gigantic sigh. Camille was, of course, absolutely right, and yet somehow each older woman felt the shame as if it were her own.

Genevieve looked at her daughter and slowly replied, "We all learned a lot that summer. I look at myself as a mom now and think about all the messes we got into when we were your age. I guess it's the only way to learn, really. Little kids, little problems; big kids, bigger problems, right?"

"Yeah, well, all I know is that I would fucking *kill* any guy who even *thought* about laying a hand on me or my friends after he drugged the shit out of us," Camille growled angrily as she choked her ponytail into a tight little bun.

Lauren looked affectionately at Genevieve's daughter and thought of her own ferocious daughters as they neared puberty. Maybe moms were finally doing a better job of teaching their girls how to be more informed and empowered. Although women of her own generation, or at least those who weren't isolated in the cocoon of religious education, were aware of how to handle or prevent mishaps, what they usually lacked was the fierce ability to speak up in the face of injustice without needing to lie to make wrongs right. She felt a glimmer of hope for the young women of today.

"I bet you would, Camille," she said lightly. "I sure wouldn't mess with you!"

TWENTY-ONE

Dancing With The Devil

"Secrets, silent, stony sit in the dark palaces of both our hearts: secrets weary of their tyranny: tyrants willing to be dethroned."

—James Joyce, *Ulysses*

I ESCORTED PATIENT NUMBER 17 into my office late in the morning, a wiry, taut-faced woman with energy to spare. Thirty-eight years old, G9P1, here for a termination at eight weeks. I'm not sure if I told you, but the G stands for *gravidity*, or the number of times that a woman has been pregnant. The P is for *parity*, the number of times that she has given birth to a fetus with a gestational age of 24 weeks or more, regardless of whether the child was born alive, stillborn, or terminated.[47] In this case, our patient had had nine pregnancies and one delivery after 24 weeks. (As we roll along in the following pages, notice both numbers and the judgments you or others might come to based on this interesting tidbit of patient information. Mark my words, you are one rare and totally zen individual if this doesn't affect your opinions in the least.)

Tara plopped down casually in my office to allow me to perform my brief history and physical before getting this show on the road. She knew the drill.

Soon, I became creepily mesmerized by this odd, charismatic woman. Keeping her on topic proved to be rather challenging as she drew me into her world.

"Do you have an escort here to take you home and give you a hand for a day or two?" I asked.

"Oh, yeah, Richard is here." She rolled her eyes and nodded toward the packed waiting room.

"Okay, that's good. I guess you're familiar with what to expect afterward?"

"Yeah, been through this lots of times. So strange, you know, especially since I prefer chicks over dicks." She laughed. Leaned forward in her chair. "Richard here, he's hopeless. He wants to spend every waking minute with me, and I can't really get rid of him. I'm def into women, but, hey, ya gotta pay the bills, right? I honestly don't know how to get rid of this guy."

Her intensity deepened as she started to tell me about her service to humanity and her own opinions on what did and did *not* turn her on. I felt my skin crawl and began to notice, not for the first time, how very stifling that windowless office could be after four or five hours. Tara recounted her life story as a drug-addicted-prostitute-turned-drug-dealer who, after many years, figured out a way to combine her talents into a multilevel business and found her niche in academic circles as a purveyor of illegal goods and services. She was articulate, penetrating, and scary. No wonder those repressed old farts found her intoxicating.

"Alrighty then," I said, smiling brightly. "I have a ton of patients out there, so thanks for filling me in, and let me know if you have any other questions!"

"Yeah, actually, I do." *Oh shit.* "How do you get rid of a rich fucking loser who's way too into you? I mean, seriously?"

I peered at her and decided I just had to ask. "Which one is Richard?"

She again pointed at the waiting room door and said, "Old White dude. You'll know who he is right away." Sure enough, I peeked into the crowded area and there he was, a balding, slightly doughy, older White man in a pullover sweater, zombie-like and desperate. My plan to talk to him evaporated faster than a cloud as I could see he was truly a man lost in the thick fog of his illusions.

Two days earlier, Richard had been stumbling through the parking garage at his place in the city, fumbling for his keys as he located his Audi. He slid into the leather interior, put his head on the steering wheel, and cried. For the first time in his life, he was losing his grip. An accomplished physicist, he could not, for the life of him, understand how in the world he had fallen into the abyss of an obsession that would very likely cost him his tenure. There he was, minding his own business after the divorce, and next thing he knew, he was down on his knees in desperate homage to a paid escort, underwear around his ankles.

It had started innocently enough. After 27 years of marriage, a man can get a little lonely and in need of some companionship when that ends, right? Surely, no real harm could come from calling a reputable escort service, and being both a novice and a gentleman, it would only seem right to take the lady out for a nice dinner and conversation before asking her to debase herself for money.

Needless to say, Richard—like so many other midlife souls—fell and fell *big time*. The brazen acuity that Tara brought into his life seared him into a jelly-legged blob of spiritual crisis. He found himself sinking deeper into the pit of sexuality and shame, unable to contain his newfound lust for more. He knew, of course he knew, that this pathetic obsession would be his undoing, and yet he continued, unable or unwilling to address the deep wounds that had brought him to this place and time.

At least that is what I envision was his story. Perhaps I am being charitable or have gone overboard. Although it can be an endless source of fascination to explore just what makes people do the things they do, I found that, in the moment, it was always far less titillating when you encountered it in real life. Most of us, with our average lives, never intermingle with the world of sex workers, drug dealers, and the like. As any nurse can tell you, it is a privilege of our profession to witness it all, and a responsibility, for sure, to be with all of it while navigating our boundaries.

TWENTY-TWO

Luz

"What we've got here is a failure to communicate."
(Lo que tenemos aquí es una falla en la comunicación.)

—The Captain, *Cool Hand Luke*

LET IT BE KNOWN that I am a huge hispanophile, one of those die-hard lovers of all things Spanish. The language, the cultures around the world, the foods, the colors. With the exception of flamenco, which always stirred my passionate heart, I only recently learned to thoroughly enjoy the repetitive rat-a-tat frenzy of Latino pop music. I must admit that it jangled my nerves until I, like so many middle-class White women, learned how to dance to it with unbridled joy in Zumba class. Now, when I hear it thumping out the windows of passing cars, I can barely resist mortifying my ever-loving family by shaking my groove thing, thoroughly convinced in my mind's eye that Shakira has *nothing* on me.

This fact, coupled with my soft heart for all the grandmothers of the world, leads me to tell you about Luz. *Luz* means "light" in Spanish, and one of my very favorite things about the Spanish language is the phrase *dar a luz*, which is how you say "give birth to." Although I wasn't quite old enough to identify with the dilemma of getting pregnant at the same time as my daughter, I could see the deep embarrassment of grandmothers who would come in as patients. Let me tell you, there is precious little uncertainty in these women about whether or not they should terminate the pregnancy. They have shifted their identities and moved on. It seems an outrage to me that so many of us have to change our blood-soaked maxi pads at the same time in our lives when we find ourselves faithfully dying our gray roots every four weeks, but there you have it. Potently fertile feminine mystique is not exclusively limited to youthful bodies.

As I write this, Luz was not much different in age than I am today, even younger, as a matter of fact. She was the reserved, often overlooked woman you might see shuffling around with a brood of kids at Walmart. Floral cotton housedress, broad sandals, gray-threaded hair pulled back into a curly ponytail with gold crowns visible on a few of her teeth. She looked tired. I barely glanced at her sitting placidly with her plaid nylon shopping bags in the waiting room on surgery day, occasionally swatting at the pesky kids buzzing around her. I just figured she was here as a support person for the young woman beside her. I was mildly surprised later when I scanned my next chart and saw that it belonged to a 48-year-old G12 P7 (remember, this is the number of pregnancies and births).

Luz shuffled into my office for her presurgical exam and consent review. Grateful for the proficient translation services of her daughter, I was able to move her along efficiently save for the awkward uncertainty about future birth control plans. When I inquired about how to prevent future pregnancies, her adult daughter Rocio (*this* beautiful name means "dewdrop"!) stopped short, and without translating this for her mother, rolled her eyes the tiniest bit and said that would not be a problem. I always hated when that happened but had little choice in being able to do much about it. Between my nonexistent Spanish and the hectic pace of a busy surgical day, these things sadly often got overlooked.

After surgery, Luz and the kids piled into the SUV—it had been a long day. Rocio started the engine, pulled out of the driveway past the few remaining protesters, and headed home. Wearily, everyone climbed out of the car and headed inside. The kids tumbled onto the couches and began arguing immediately about which video game they should play.

"Mami, *porfa*! Go sit down!" Rocio said, exasperated as her mother shuffled slowly into the kitchen to reheat the empanadas she had made yesterday.

"The kids are starving, and your father hasn't eaten all day," Luz replied, slightly aghast at the thought of sitting and doing nothing. To tell the truth, she wondered why everyone was making a fuss. Twelve pregnancies and seven children of her own, she felt like she usually did as she bled heavily into the doubled-up maternity pads that she was instructed to put into her polka-dotted *bombachas* before being discharged from the clinic. Luz was so used to soaking pads and passing clots that she didn't see the point of being pampered today. No one worried about it any other time, so how was this different?

"Ay, Mami, just go sit." Rocio twisted the oven dial and arranged the dumplings on the baking tray before popping them into the oven. She was tired too. Ever since her parents arrived last year from Argentina, she'd felt completely drained. When her dad could no longer work on the farm due to a back injury, Rocio told herself that it would be great to have her parents and three younger siblings move in with her here in the States. She had missed them terribly, and besides, it would certainly be helpful to have her mom around to help with her own two kids. But even though this had ended up being true, trying to bridge endless cultural and language barriers proved to be exhausting as she worked to ensure that her parents and little brothers and sister didn't struggle as she had when she emigrated alone to the U.S. nearly nine years before.

Luz walked quietly into the small living room and sat down. Slightly embarrassed, she stole a glance at her husband. Jose kept his eyes firmly on the newspaper, avoiding her gaze. The kids squabbled over the game controllers and a shouting match soon began.

"I *said* your time's up, you moron!"

"It hasn't even been five minutes! I just got to level four!"

"*Mario Kart* is *lame*! Let's play *The Simpsons: Road Rage*!"

"I'm hungry, Abuela. ¿Cuándo cenamos?" whined Jorge.

At that, Jose snapped his newspaper shut and exploded at the kids. "*¡Cállate la boca!*" He was sick and tired of the bickering. It had, indeed, been a long day, like every other day since he had arrived in this country. After an endless succession of useless days, Jose longed for fresh air and hard work. Completely unprepared for city life, he spent his days sitting with a heating pad in the recliner, and several evenings a week he met a few compadres at the corner bar. At 51 years old, his current existence could not have been further from what he had always envisioned his life would be: a prosperous farm, loving family, and good health in his beautiful homeland. Although he was most grateful to his industrious daughter, this life was wholly unacceptable save for the fact that he had nowhere else to go.

He rubbed his eyes and thought proudly of Rocio, his oldest daughter, and undoubtedly his favorite. It was true that he had missed her terribly when she, at the ripe age of 17, earned a full scholarship to university and never returned. He remembered with immense pride how, even as a young girl, she eagerly studied and socked away every peso by selling her home-baked goods at the side of the road. She had always had big dreams and big plans, that *hijita*. Jose never understood her desire to leave the country, but he could not help being amazed at her fearless ambition to do so. Looking around the tidy row house that she now proudly called home, he felt deeply conflicted. Both gratitude and humiliation welled up together in his heart as he did his best to silently cope with his circumstances.

Dinner was the loud, energetic affair it usually was except for the moment when little Florencia toddled over to Luz for her usual evening lap bounce. Luz gently helped her scramble up and jiggled her leg cautiously. "No, Abuela. ¡Esforzate! *Harder!*" she screamed and started pounding her chubby fists into her grandmother's belly. Luz shielded her stomach while

Rocio quickly grabbed the child and sat her down hard in her big girl booster seat at the table. Florencia widened her already enormous brown eyes in shock before letting out her legendary Guinness Book of World Records scream to show her outrage.

Later that night, in their tiny bedroom, Luz laid a thick towel on her side of the bed before sinking down on it into the soft mattress. Jose sat on the edge of the bed, unsure if this was going to be similar or different from other womanly troubles after so many pregnancies.

"Um, will you be okay?" he murmured in Spanish as he looked down at his wife.

"Yes, I think so," she replied as she adjusted the hot compress on her belly. "The doctor told me that my womb is very floppy, like a soggy balloon. He told me to stop getting pregnant because it is dangerous."

"Well, what are we to do?" Jose asked, genuinely worried for his wife's health but also for yet another loss in his flat existence. He was no young buck, but he did still mightily enjoy the release he felt into her soft body when they made love.

"Do not worry, *mi amor*. The nurse gave me some pills that will keep me from getting pregnant again. I will start using them tomorrow." Luz patted his hand and Jose promptly fell asleep.

In a typical Argentinian household, yerba mate (pronounced MAH-tay), with its 24 vitamins and minerals, along with tons of antioxidants and caffeine, is an essential part of every family morning ritual. The next morning, as always, the family gathered around to share the hot, steaming liquid that gave them a brief moment of togetherness at the start of each day.

"Who's turn is it to be *cebador* today?" Rocio sang out. Everyone took turns being the one who was in charge of the mate, and the kids always jostled for the honor.

Little Martina's hand shot up in the air. "It's me!" she said eagerly, then proceeded to take the first sips through the *bombilla*, the filtering straw, before passing the cup to each family member, refilling it as she went. There was a cozy and very familiar murmur of sipping and shuffling in the small kitchen that marked the beginning of another busy day.

With her precious birth control pills in hand, Luz moved apart from the group and carefully tucked one pill into the packed yerba mate leaves in her cup before pouring the boiling hot water over it all and letting it steep before drinking. She congratulated herself on thinking of something she did religiously every day and pairing that with her pill taking, as the nurse had suggested. She felt confident that this would be a surefire way not to forget to take one pill every day as directed. And at 60 dollars per pack, she would need to decide which days to use them since she couldn't be sure that they would be able to afford them for very long.

I was very pleased to see Luz's name on my roster of follow-up patients several weeks after her procedure. She was, indeed, correct in her understanding that her uterus was on the floppy side after having had so many pregnancies, and a real concern was monitoring for extremely heavy bleeding post-abortion. I wanted to make sure that she was healing safely.

My heart sank when I went into her exam room and saw that

the translator she had brought along was none other than her 11-year-old daughter, Martina. I asked the child if anyone else could translate, but she shook her head and said that everyone else was at work. I bit my lip for a moment and remembered the righteous outrage of my nursing students when they found out that not all health-care facilities employed the use of translators, either on staff or by phone. We did, in fact, have several Spanish-speaking staff members, but on quiet days like this, they weren't always there. And even though phone translation is accessible nowadays, I can assure you it is not consistently used for a variety of reasons. I took a big breath and did my best.

"How are you feeling? How is your bleeding?" I asked, opening with some simple questions.

Martina gravely turned to her mother and dutifully relayed the questions. Luz answered, and I was happy to hear that her bleeding was minimal and she was feeling well.

"Are you taking the birth control pills that I gave you? How are you taking them?" I asked.

After a confused pause, Martina asked her mother as best she could, and Luz replied that she was putting them in her mate and all was well.

I had no idea what she meant, as I had no familiarity with mate. Assuming it was some kind of food, I asked her if she was swallowing it, and of course the answer was "yes." What I did not know was that she was swallowing hot herbal tea, but not the undissolvable pills that were stuffed amid the leaves. Oh no, *oh no*, epic fail on my part. And my ineptitude only got worse as I plowed on.

I spoke slowly and with plenty of pauses, using the simplest words I could find, praying that this poor child would be able to convey the most important instructions to her mother.

"You should get your normal period within the next two to six weeks. If you don't get it in the next two months, give us a call." (At this time, I still did not know she was failing to take her pills.) "It is now safe to resume all your normal activities, including sex, but be very, very careful because you can get pregnant again right away." Martina listened carefully, then stumbled over the words as best she could, and I continued. "Be sure to use extra protection, like condoms, whenever you have missed a pill or if you vomit up your pill one day. If you miss a pill, take it as soon as you remember. You can double up and take two pills the next day if that is when you remember."

How confusing did that *sound? Oh, how I felt like an incompetent piece of shit trying to bridge the language barrier, especially in trying to converse through the patient's child.* "Do you have a doctor or clinic you can go to for follow-up care? No? Okay, here is the address and phone number for your nearest Planned Parenthood. They will help you to cover what you can't afford."

As they left, I hung my head in shame. Long before the advent of Google Translate, there was no way I could possibly learn even the basics of the multitude of languages that patients spoke when they came for care. While we tried hard to advise patients to bring trusted adults as translators, they could only do the best they could. And it is critically important to note that even *if* we now have better access to translation materials in this day and age, cultural misunderstandings still abound. I tried to distribute written instructions in at least Spanish whenever possible, but too often, I could sense a level of illiteracy as women politely hid their lack of understanding as they folded up these indecipherable papers and went on their way.

We saw Luz several months later, pregnant again. This time, Rocio was able to figure out what had gone wrong, and she already had an appointment at Planned Parenthood for Luz to undergo a tubal ligation. I would love to say that this was the only time that anything like this happened under my watch, but I am not given to fictionalizing tidy truths about my experiences to absolve myself or offer a nice literary cleanup to give my dear readers a sense of resolution. I look to my idealistic and energetic young colleagues to charge in with brilliant new ideas so these sad situations can be a thing of the past.

If this sounds cynical or sarcastic, it's not meant to be. I am a big believer in the Zen concept of *shoshin*, or beginner's mind. For it is in there, through the fresh eyes of the novice, that new ideas are birthed. As we gain experience and, yes, wisdom, it is too often accompanied by a sense of helplessness and overwhelm. When you encounter surly, closed-off health-care professionals, I hope that you can find it in your heart to imagine them at some point in their careers being hopeful, principled, and caring. It may not help them, but it might help you shrug off any negativity toward others as you navigate the system.

TWENTY-THREE

Elena

"I still have a little impostor syndrome…It doesn't go away, that feeling that you shouldn't take me that seriously. What do I know? I share that with you because we all have doubts in our abilities, about our power and what that power is."

–Michelle Obama, *in London, December 2018*

A FRIEND OF MINE just completed her SANE certification, which stands for Sexual Assault Nurse Examiner. She, like so many nurse warriors, feels drawn to serving rape victims in their moment of need as police and emergency department personnel continue to ineptly—or even downright abusively—bungle their investigations and subsequent medical care. According to the International Association of Forensic Nurses, the certification program has been in place since 2002, and as of 2020 there have been about 1,700 nurses certified in the U.S.[48]

Once again, I laud these fearless nurses who confidently stride into the thick of the crime scene aftermath to flick off the incompetent bumblers around them as they simultaneously shield, treat, and gather evidence from their patients. I had zero desire to do that work, and nothing could have prepared me for the day when I had to at least try.

Early on in my tenure, I was in the midst of one of my usual crazy surgery days when Marilyn stopped me as I was running down the hallway to see my next preoperative patient.

"Hey, Patrice, I need to talk to you." Marilyn's bright blue-green eyes had an even more piercing quality than usual as she looked intently at me.

"What's up?"

"I put a patient in exam room two. She's a walk-in. You need to see her right away."

I was a little put out. "Why would we see her on a surgery day? It's crazy right now! Try to fit her in for my office visit day on Thursday, okay?" I started walking back toward the throng of waiting patients, but Marilyn grabbed my arm.

"No, she needs to be seen today. This is an emergency."

Oh shit. "Well, then she should see Dr. Atkins, right? Let's call him out of the OR."

Marilyn continued to peer at me in that odd, intense way.

"No, it has to be you."

"Marilyn, what is going *on*?" This was getting stranger by the minute. For crying out loud, why was I, a newly minted nurse practitioner, the only person for the job?

She pulled me aside and gave me the story. It seemed that this woman, I'll call her Elena, came in off the street insisting that she desperately needed help. In Marilyn's office, she tearfully told her that she had been raped almost a week earlier. Having told no one else, she had been curled up in her room ever since, overcome with shame and horror at what had happened.

I backed away in dismay. "Oh, no, I'm really not qualified to do this. She needs to be seen by a trained specialist."

"She won't go. I tried talking to her about this, but she is terrified and said she cannot do this again. If she doesn't get seen today, she will never get the courage to go again."

This struck me as a tad melodramatic. "Well, my license is on the line. I don't even know what meds to prescribe!"

"Patrice, sorry to say this, but you're it. This woman put her trust in us, and she will not leave until we at least try. Do your best." This was not a request.

I dove into my office and frantically began looking up what lab tests I would need to do and which antibiotics would need to be prescribed to prevent or treat suspected sexually transmitted infections. My hands were visibly shaking as I smoothed my lab coat before entering the exam room.

Elena sat on the end of the table. An unremarkable woman of about 35, the only thing I really remember about her were the braces on her teeth. As an adult, I had also decided to get my teeth straightened and still wore a retainer at night. This seemingly inconsequential fact chiseled its way into my awareness, forcing me to see us as peers. We could easily have swapped places at that moment in time. And no matter how terrified I felt, it was far better to be me than her at the moment. I cleared my throat and introduced myself.

"So, Marilyn tells me that you had an unfortunate incident last week, and you're here now for some follow-up. Can you tell me a little about what happened?"

Elena lifted her panic-stricken eyes and began her story. She had been out with a girlfriend at a local bar for an early dinner and drinks. Just after they parted ways in the parking lot, a man grabbed her from behind, shoved her into the nearby bushes, and raped her.

"And so, now you'd like to be checked for infections or pregnancy?" I ventured, trying to surmise what she wanted from me.

"Well, yes, and there's something else." She covered her face with her hands and started to cry. Softly she said, "I... I think there's something still inside me."

"You mean like a condom or something?"

"I was on my period, and I was wearing a tampon. I begged him to please give me a second to take it out, but he...he didn't care. I haven't been able to check if it's still there. I feel so ashamed." She started to cry again, and I felt like smashing someone in the face.

"Oh, well, let's see, okay?"

I guided her to lie down on the exam table and put her feet in the stirrups. As I slid my gloved finger into her vagina, the tampon was immediately palpable. I grabbed the string and pulled. I think we both cried with relief, but it was short-lived as the gut-wrenching smell of rotting decay bowled us both over while I wrapped the slimy tampon in layer after layer of paper towels before discarding it in a plastic trash bag. To hell with DNA samples, I thought grimly.

Elena fell into my arms, crying hysterically with relief. I hugged her back, weak in the knees as much from release as from the fetid odor that was beginning to subside.

We pulled ourselves together, and I asked her if she wanted

to press charges. She said no; she just wanted to get on with her life. I told her that I was absolutely not the most qualified professional to help her in this situation and gave her the name and number of the rape crisis hotline, urging her to follow up with them for proper care. I wrote her some prescriptions for broad-spectrum antibiotics that I hoped would keep her from getting a systemic blood infection from her retained tampon, and after a tearful goodbye, I left the room.

Later that day, Marilyn stopped by my office. I gave her a weary look as she sat down.

"How are you doing?" she asked.

I smiled wanly. "That was the worst experience of my life, thank you very much."

Marilyn leaned forward. "What you did today saved that woman's life. There was no one else in the world she would've trusted to help her in that moment."

I was not and am still not so sure. I did my best, but I didn't feel like a hero at all. Who knows how much better off she'd have been if she'd been seen by a fully trained professional? All I can say is that she gave *me* the precious gift of willing myself to be present when my whole self wanted to turn and run.

Part Three

"Doctors heal, or try to, but as nurses we step into the breach, figure out what needs to be done for any given patient today, on this shift, and then, with love and exasperation, do it as best we can."

—Theresa Brown, *Critical Care*

SEVERAL FINAL STORIES LINGER in my memory that remind me of my eternal frustration in not always being able to provide the kind of sexual health care that I find acceptable. Sometimes it was just so complicated and downright painful. These were, hands down, the hardest things I've ever encountered as an abortion nurse. Frankly, this first story ranks among the top five worst scenarios I've dealt with in my entire career that has spanned nearly four decades. Don't worry though; in the second story, I'll slide you toward home with one that isn't particularly terrible but gives you a thought-provoking indication of what burnout looks like as it rattles your cage and shows you the door.

TWENTY-FOUR

Kendra

"In the modern world we have invented ways of speeding up invention, and people's lives change so fast that a person is born into one kind of world, grows up in another, and by the time his children are growing up, lives in still a different world."

—Margaret Mead, *People and Places*

TO ROUND OUT THE age ranges that made my work so interesting, allow me to introduce my youngest patient, Kendra. At 11 years old, my heart skipped more than one beat as I learned about this youngster who had traveled from several states away with her mom to have a late-term abortion. As I've told you, I am not trained in—nor do I have any practical experience—working with little kids beyond the basics of nursing school back in the '80s. I straightened my lab coat and squared my shoulders just before tapping on Marilyn's office door to introduce myself as requested.

"Oh, here she is. Come in, come in." Marilyn gestured to me as I entered to find a very professionally attired woman with perfect posture balanced delicately on the edge of her chair with a sweet-faced, chubby little girl perched placidly to her left.

"This is the nurse practitioner I was telling you about. Patrice, this is Tamara and her daughter, Kendra," Marilyn continued with steely eyes that admonished me not to overreact.

"It's nice to meet you," I replied warily. To say that people were tiptoeing on eggshells would be an understatement. I got the distinct impression that mom and administrator had worked extensively to come to an agreement for how things would be handled. Both knew, however, that licensed professionals are often loose cannons who can and often do throw a monkey wrench into the most delicate of negotiations. Personality quirks aside, the reason for this is often clear to us at least. Unlike unlicensed professionals, we are acutely aware that if we violate regulatory statutes, at best we might lose our licenses, and in the worst-case scenario, we can go to jail for failing to report potential child abuse. Regardless of their machinations, it was my job to assess the situation independently and move forward accordingly.

Marilyn was uncharacteristically authoritative as she outlined how Kendra's case would be handled. When speaking to me, she alternated between intense eye contact and looking away, a very confusing and most unusual interaction in our normally collegial relationship. "So, we'll let you know how and when it will be time for you to do your preoperative assessment," she concluded as she ushered me out the door without getting a word in edgewise. I arched one eyebrow at her as I left the room quietly.

When it was my turn to play my part, I called Kendra and

her mom in for the preoperative assessment. Because she was so late term, she would need several days of slow cervical dilation, so this gave me some time to get to know her before the actual surgery. In these cases, the doctors would insert laminaria tents, which are small rods of sterilized seaweed that expand in the cervical canal to gradually and gently open the cervix.[49] I ushered mother and daughter into the exam room as Tamara, ever calm, articulate, and collected, nonetheless eyed me nervously.

The history and physical examination were unremarkable. I learned nothing that the chart hadn't outlined, and that was fine with me. I was certainly not looking for trouble. I trusted Marilyn, and Tamara was certainly impeccable, but something about the situation troubled me. I asked Tamara to step out for a moment while I finished up with her daughter. She drew back in a flash of indignation, then quickly resumed her gracious demeanor before leaving the room, no doubt to stride into Marilyn's office for an explanation of this impertinent change in the plan of which she had been assured. I might add here that in addition to the emotional aspect of this ordeal, several thousand dollars were at stake.

I looked at the docile and withdrawn child sitting on the exam table before asking what countless other grown-ups had already asked her. Kendra was well rehearsed and answered slowly.

"I know everyone has already asked you this, but I have to ask again. Tell me how you got pregnant."

"My friend and I were playing around, and we did what we saw on the internet. We won't do it again." Kendra repeated her transgression flatly, clearly bored and annoyed at having to apologize yet again. She paused a moment before asking, "Can I bring Ezra with me when I get my surgery?"

"Um, who's Ezra?"

Kendra silently pointed to a small, well-worn flannel blanket with a playful pattern of monkeys and other assorted jungle animals on it. Tears sprung to my eyes. I gently replied that I would ask but that it'd probably be okay.

Tamara and Marilyn both heaved huge sighs of relief as I escorted Kendra back to the office and asked Marilyn to check with Dr. Gross to see if she could bring her buddy Ezra into the operating room. Kendra smiled shyly as I made the request on her behalf, and things went according to plan. I am still completely unsure about this patient, her family, and the events that led up to her needing an abortion at age 11. The fact that it was late term did not surprise me in the least. I know that recently there has been much speculation and discussion about the morality and legality of late-term abortions, and I've already outlined the many reasons why these rare cases occur. In the case of very young children, pregnancy is often detected rather late in the game, with kids like Kendra going to GI specialists for supposed gastrointestinal issues long before even considering going to an OB-GYN.

TWENTY-FIVE

First Impressions

*"We all have too many wheels, screws, and valves to judge
each other on first impressions or one or two pointers. I don't
understand you, you don't understand me, and we don't
understand ourselves."*

—Anton Chekhov, *Ivanov*

NOT LONG AGO, I attended an inservice program about human
trafficking. Even though my years of working in the clinic were
long behind me, I felt and still feel a gnawing, sickening sensa-
tion in my gut as I recalled how utterly naive and completely
inept I had been in identifying—let alone intervening in—this
horrifyingly common arena of women's health. According to
Humanrightsfirst.org, more than 71 percent of trafficking victims are female, the majority of whom are forced into hospi-
tality or domestic work, with a grim 19 percent of women and
girls being used for the risky but substantially more profitable
sex trade.[50]

You might think that any good and caring clinician would get some Spidey-Sense about this. While I would agree that this does sometimes happen, in such a busy environment it's not a guarantee. I am absolutely certain that I missed more than my share of trafficked women. And truthfully, as I've confessed before, I rarely went looking for trouble. What one does with one's hunch can mean life or death and a whole lot of paperwork. I can also verify that sometimes what is surmised can be dead wrong, a puzzle not easily solved by the limits of our own worldviews and assumptions.

One day, I was finishing up my follow-up appointments when I heard a bit of a commotion at the front desk. I couldn't make out what was being said, but it was definitely a heated exchange, mostly a loud male voice followed by murmured female voices and the sound of a chart being slammed onto a desk. As expected, Kimberly, our receptionist, rounded the corner and promptly warned me that the next patient's escort was not only a major pain in the ass, but she suspected that he was abusive as well. As she was a recent women's studies grad from Sarah Lawrence, I knew not to take her words lightly. I thanked her for the heads-up and proceeded with my appointments.

Eventually, I met the dreaded duo. I slipped into the exam room to find a middle-aged man with salt-and-pepper hair with a young woman, 22 years old according to her chart, fully dressed in traditional Indian garb. The woman sat quietly on my exam stool while the man paced frantically around the room, mumbling in what I guessed was Hindi. I took a deep breath and introduced myself.

"Hello. My name is Patrice, and I will be—"

"Just get on with it!" The man's outburst, coupled with the snarl and sneer on his face, was charming, to say the least.

Ignoring him, I turned to my patient and addressed her directly. "Aadhya, how are you feeling since your surgery?"

Aadhya smiled timidly as she nodded and said she was fine. I was glad that she understood what I had asked, but, being a language learner myself, I knew that it didn't rule out the possibility that her English was limited to basic pleasantries. At that moment, her male companion stepped between us, interjecting, "Good. Can we go now?"

"Excuse me, but what relation are you to Aadhya?"

"I am her *husband*. Not that it's any of your business."

I looked at my patient, who avoided eye contact but gave a tiny nod of her head.

"I need to do a quick exam, and then you are free to go. Please step outside the room, and she will be done momentarily." My voice was firm as I showed him the door. He looked at me as if I were nothing more than a stray dog that had just peed on his shoe.

"I will stay. She cannot be left alone since she doesn't speak much English."

"Oh, thanks for the heads-up. If you could just explain that she needs to undress from the waist down—"

"I will tell her as you do whatever it is you have to do. You don't seem to be listening. She cannot be left alone."

Our eyes locked in a steely standoff. I wanted him out of that room, and he wasn't budging. Slowly, I turned my gaze to Aadhya who continued to sit in the corner with her eyes demurely cast downward. This scenario seemed quite familiar to her. What to do? We did not have a security guard on regular appointment days, and the local police, as helpful as they were on the rare occasions we called, were not likely to get involved in this. I had very little recourse, and they knew it. The National Human Trafficking Hotline would not be established until several years later, a real pity as I reflect now on the lack of essential resources at the time. I knew that I had to be really careful about reporting any suspicions since patient privacy laws mandate confidentiality, *and* reporting can often lead to further abuse as cases are investigated.

I eyed my opponent carefully. "Tell me, what is your name?"

He hesitated for a tenth of a second, realizing that if he didn't tell me, there would be trouble. Fleeting panic spread over his face before he said evenly, "My name is Dave."

"Well, *Dave*, I suggest that you step out of the room. The sooner you leave, the sooner we will be finished." Eyes glittering with hatred, he stormed out of the room and slammed the door.

I heaved a large sigh of relief as I watched him go and turned toward my patient. *Finally*, I thought. *Let's get to the bottom of this!*

"Aadhya, before we get started, tell me a little about yourself. Do you feel safe at home?"

She cleared her throat before nodding yes, then said defensively in perfect English, "I...I don't know why you all are so mean to him. Devesh is only trying to help me." She tilted her head from side to side emphatically, clearly annoyed at this confusing nonsense.

I paused, startled. As I looked deeply into her eyes, I saw a potential life story unfold. In a few seconds, a story so very unfamiliar and yet compelling revealed itself to me in the brief moment that I allowed my imagination to open before figuring out what to do next.

I saw a 19-year-old girl living in India. She was raised in a traditionally old-school family, and despite pressure to do something more prestigious, she aspired only to work in retail surrounded by beautiful fabrics or fragrant perfumes. She wasn't terribly good at anything, and with only average looks and a shy, thoughtful personality, she was rather content when her parents started looking for a potential husband for her.

Fast forward three years, she found herself living in the United States, married to a guy she had only met once before her wedding day. Even though some of her friends thought she was crazy to agree to a marriage arranged by her parents, she was okay with it. How was it really so different from using a dating site to find someone that met all her standards? Was a software algorithm any better than her parents who really knew her and also had her best interests at heart? True, Devesh could be annoying sometimes, but underneath all the bluster was a sweet and scared man who mistrusted so much in life. He was a glass-half-empty kind of guy, and the only thing he wanted was to be by her side.

I snapped myself out of my reverie and got back down to business. A quick exam revealed nothing remarkable, and we talked about birth control methods, very few of which were familiar to her. She asked if her husband could come back in the room to discuss their options.

Dave or Devesh strutted back into the room. He began interrogating her rapidly in Hindi, and she answered softly. We agreed to give birth control pills a try, with a clear warning that she could become pregnant again right away so they should use a condom and/or spermicide before the pills took effect.

As I gathered a couple of sample pill packs and condoms for them, I realized I might have completely misread Aadhya's situation, and I was no longer sure of what I saw, either through my direct observations or my inner assessment. Believe it or not, this was the beginning of the end for me as a women's health provider. It's not that I don't love a good comeuppance and a chance to topple my biases. In fact, this was the very thing that never ceased to delight and amaze me in my chosen career, as it offered me so many glimpses into the many and varied complexities of the human condition.

No. Sorry to disappoint or shatter anyone's illusion of the tireless champion who sets out to right the injustices of the world, but it was the overtiredness of hoping, at the end of the day, that I would be able to get a good night's sleep that night. That I had done most things right or at least the things that mattered. As the condition known as burnout sets in, both everything and nothing matter while numb exhaustion persists.

TWENTY-SIX

The End Of An Era

"The Eagles ended on a rather abrupt note,
although in retrospect I realize now that it had been
ending for quite some time."

—**Don Henley,** ***Modern Drummer, vol. 14***

AFTER ABOUT THREE YEARS of working full-time in the clinic, I pulled into the driveway one morning as I did every day amid the protesters clamoring for the rights of the unborn and walked into the packed waiting room full of desperate young people. There, it hit me. I was done. As I threaded my way through the throng, the futility of it all smacked me right between the eyes. I peeked between the slats of the heavy blinds on the clinic windows and realized that the people outside were the parents and grandparents of the people *inside*, and the senselessness of it tipped the balance toward me turning in my resignation. Besides, the clinic kept messing with my schedule to accommodate the whims of our almost-retired doctor, whose new passion for custom sports car competitions dictated his availability, and this was screwing with my day care needs way too much. As usual, my motives were a combination of annoyed social justice and pure pragmatism.

Ultimately, though, I felt like I was a weary soldier-for-hire in a war that was raging on with no end in sight. Years and years of activists on both sides passionately waving banners, pointing fingers, and avenging murders had worn me down. Battles that were being fought—and that continue to be fought—in the highest courts in the land, missives about the horror of abortion, or the equally devastating cautionary *Handmaid's Tale* apocalypse catalyzed people again and again into taking sides. I was beyond caring and frankly just wanted some peace and quiet.

I saw no end in sight, and I was exhausted. I felt myself becoming less and less compassionate for the dozens of young women who passed through my office. They just never stopped. The truth was that there was nothing I could do that would stem the tidal wave of unintended pregnancies no matter how much I tried. I now know that the work isn't about me trying to stem the flow of life curling back on itself.

In spite of the recent decline in reported sexual intercourse over the last 10 years—with a huge increase in the number of Americans (particularly young men) between the ages of 18 and 29 reporting no sex in 2018, doubling since 2008[51]—there's still a whopping majority who are having good old penile-vaginal intercourse that can lead to pregnancy. Mind you, I am saddened about the declining rates of sexual activity for young people, which dropped at an alarming rate between 2008 and 2018, and this is driven, as my research suggests, by economic, social, and technologic factors that often increase physical isolation. The joy of genuine intimacy can never be underestimated or replaced. If anything, I would love to find a way to promote *more* physical relationships in the world, not fewer!

I would like to think that common sense drives most people to agree that part of the answer, as discussed in previous chapters, lies not only in effective sexual health education but also accessibility to reliable, affordable birth control. And, in fact, a recent Gallup poll shows that a full 91 percent of Americans feel that birth control is morally acceptable.[52] However, there's still a nagging 10 percent of women who risk unintended pregnancy by not using any kind of contraception, with the highest percentage of that group (18 percent) being teens between the ages of 15 and 19.[53]

And, not to point fingers, but with a sizable number of kids attending Catholic or conservative Christian schools, there's a good chance that they are not receiving much, if any, reliable information about sexual health. I vividly remember, with great fondness, my daughter coming home from college and telling me about a lively argument she had had with her roommate, a *premed major*, about how lemonade is *not* going to help prevent a pregnancy if you drink it or even douche with it after unprotected sex. This fine young woman, a product of Catholic education, was convinced that she was right, her rationale being that the acidity would change your body's pH enough to prevent fertilization. She has since gone on to become an OB-GYN, and I often wonder if her decision was motivated in any way by her realization of the severe lack of information she had had until she hit medical school.

I am not exaggerating when I say, too, that the misinformation that people are getting is appalling. One day my mail carrier
mixed up my mail with that of my sweet, elderly neighbor, and
I inadvertently got a glossy informative flyer from our neighborhood Catholic church. I was transfixed reading the shocking
misinformation about contraception—not to mention abortion—with gems warning that science tells us that birth control
not only leads to skyrocketing nonmarital births but that it can
also kill you. There were beautiful photos and quotes about the
sanctity and beauty of a life morally lived according to God's
plan. It was so sickeningly seductive that I went right over to my
desk and wrote a check to Planned Parenthood.

But I digress. As I write this, I remind myself of the
tireless advocates, courageous providers, researchers, and legal
geniuses who have devoted their entire lives to giving women
a choice in arguably one of the most important aspects of their
lives. And I salute them with every fiber of my being, deeply
grateful not only for their undying devotion, but for giving me
the chance to walk among them for a few years. As I warned you,
I was no hero, just a busy working mom trying to contribute to
the well-being of the people I served as I strived for the work-life
balance so treasured by most of us. And I grew weary of the pain
and confusion, but mostly of the secrecy and shame.

My reluctance to share where I worked with the other moms
on the playground was born not only of a fear of my kids or
me being frozen out of the social scene, but more importantly
for those among them who paled when they saw me come into
their exam room, knowing that they would see me on the soccer
field the following week. If you tried to guess who in your casual

social circle might have been my patient on any given day, you would very likely be wrong. And while I am not a big secret keeper, this is one area where secrets will go to my grave with me. It is so very sad that these women bear such a heavy burden with so little community support.

I became more and more intrigued by the idea of transforming a classroom into a place of genuine exchange for nurses to grow and change, and I found myself gravitating back to the university to teach some of what I had learned. While the work was cleaner, it most definitely was not easier, nor were the hours less demanding. However, I was able to craft a life that suited me better, and so I took my talents there full-time while limiting my clinical practice to a few hours a week, seeing only the two-week follow-up patients. I also chose to work in the big city, glad to be an anonymous provider for people I would likely never see again.

TWENTY-SEVEN

Toppled

*"If others tell us something we make assumptions,
and if they don't tell us something we make assumptions
to fulfill our need to know and to replace the need to
communicate. Even if we hear something and we don't
understand we make assumptions about what it means and
then believe the assumptions."*

—don Miguel Ruiz, *The Four Agreements*

I END MY STORY the way I began, with no clear explanation of right and wrong or even a sense of purpose other than to give you a glimpse into the abortion world as I experienced it, feeling into the nooks and crannies of my memories and growing them into stories that are as real to me as to any writer of fiction who weaves tales so compelling that they become beloved and carefully crafted creations of their imaginations.

What I will leave you with, though, is the journey I've taken that has shaken my core beliefs and led me to a place of peace that transcends the angst and agony. It has required me to suspend my disbelief of far-fetched notions and at times go beyond my practical and professional knowledge, which I have offered you, dear reader, with great love and appreciation for all that my hard-earned education and experience have given me.

Fittingly, for me, it started with a story that I came upon many years ago, which has been sitting in a dusty, quiet corner of my mind during my busy years of working, raising a family, and caring for my parents before their deaths. The story tumbled back into my consciousness one day as I came across an interesting article about several well-respected psychiatrists and psychologists who have risked their professional status to explore and then publish their work on past life regression, which flies in the face of conventional scientific and religious thought in the modern world. I eagerly snapped up their books, and the sense of being upended rattled me yet again as I felt in myself a sense of knowing, at least for me, that this is and has always been my Truth as well. It is not for everyone; I firmly believe that each of us comes to our own conclusions in our own unique ways, which is in fact the way it is meant to be. So take what resonates and leave the rest.

I have long suspected that, just as my assumptions about the people I meet are often not accurate, it is also not true that abortion has always been and must remain the huge deal that society has made it out to be. The drama, the chest-beating, and desperation are an illusion that we humans have placed on it in this moment in history. We are here to honor the struggle, and for many, this is a real and necessary step in their personal progress as human beings as they fight wholeheartedly in their quest to protect or preserve life as they see it.

The heartbreak and frustration of seeing budding humans being denied their one shot at life is terrifying, or it can give rise to
a lifetime of anger, shame, and guilt. But what if, as many faith
traditions around the world would suggest, we get many more
lifetimes? I think of the incredibly brave patient on that PBS
documentary who shared her apology to the twin fetuses she
chose to abort, saying that she was deeply honored that they had
chosen her but that she had to decline their offer at the moment.

I am actually not sure where the official doctrines of Ju-
deo-Christian beliefs renouncing the notion of reincarnation
originate, but suffice to say that millions of people in the world
today reject reincarnation as being heretical nonsense, and not
just from a religious perspective. The scientific and medical
communities soundly discredit the notion of working with the
principle of past lives as not only ridiculous but dangerous, as
many believe that doing this merely feeds into delusions and the
possibility of retrieving memories that are not real, at least not in
the conventional sense.

And yet, in my work as a nurse, I've come to walk the line
between conventional wisdom and that which goes beyond our
limited understanding of the world around us. I cannot under-
estimate the possibilities of healing through deep recognition of
the human experiences that exceed empirical knowledge, even if
they can't be quantified and explored in a logical way, so long as
there is a deep sense of integrity and love for ourselves and the
processes that unfold within us.

There are a plethora of New Age healing practices in this day
and age, and it has certainly been interesting to see how people

today grapple with their issues through all kinds of modalities—some bringing genuine growth or healing while others are outright scams. In any case, it is safe to say that people are yearning for and exploring therapies that go far beyond conventional medical care, and I am certainly open to exploration as well, with the caveat that along with genuine curiosity, a strong sense of oneself is essential for the journey.

Back to the final story I am about to tell you. It stayed safely tucked away until I came across an intriguing short seminar by Dr. Linda Backman, a longtime licensed psychologist with years of documented experiences doing past life regression hypnotherapy.[54] She described the experiences of thousands of patients who were able to detail past lifetimes during their sessions, and how doing so often provided deeply meaningful insights about their current lifetime struggles and purposes for being here.

She is not alone. I found myself diving deeply into the work of other powerhouses like Brian Weiss, Ian Stephenson, and Helen Wambach, uncovering a bevy of clinical researchers known for their work in past life regression. Not two days after I wrote this, I discovered that there's an entire department at a mainstream medical school that devotes itself to exploring this very topic, and to my chagrin, I also learned about a movie that just came out this month that parallels my final story with alarming similarity.

My closing tale is not new, especially at this juncture in time. When people are forced out of their bubbles to grapple with concepts and situations beyond their usual frame of reference, all kinds of stories emerge. As with so much in this divergent world at the moment, there will be vociferous disbelievers and fervent devotees in the reincarnation debate, and again, I grow weary of the skirmishes and find my serenity in walking lightly down the middle of the road with both extremes taking strolls with me at one time or another, much like interesting colleagues who don't take themselves too seriously.

Because even as the skeptic in me shakes my head at this, another side of me gets shivers down my spine and I can't help but acknowledge how deeply healing this has been for me and probably countless others. Dr. Backman, along with a surprising number of other board-certified contemporaries who have also added regression therapy to their practices, has described many cases of patients being able to release inexplicable shame, guilt, and anger as they begin to unravel stories of past lives that have led them to where they are today. And, as she openly acknowledges, it really doesn't matter if one remains unconvinced; healing is healing. As noted by the powerful Brené Brown, shame begins to disintegrate when we tell our stories.

The essence of the story, even if the details are fuzzy, gives credence to our feelings around what we perceive as our most shameful secrets. Even if it is just a fantasy to believe that one had been, say, someone's abusive mother in a past life, when they are now dealing with a rebellious and angry teenager, the release that often comes from this kind of exploration can prove invaluable as the person works through their own victim and tyrant issues with a trained therapist. It doesn't matter if the pain and confusion take shape as a very specific past life experience, although that can be very, very helpful. The pain and confusion are real now, and as many indigenous cultures have known for millennia, healing current energy can have a huge impact for

THE VIEW FROM THE CLINIC

many generations to come.

Not long ago, I was chatting with one of my favorite people, a longtime emergency room nurse with whom I share a love for the absurd situations we often found ourselves in. She is a wizened old cynic and, like so many other emergency room nurses, has seen almost everything in her particular line of work. As I talked to her about the possibility of reincarnation and how, for me, it is a complete game changer when I think about the desperation and finality we all struggle with, she kind of rolled her eyes a bit then bit her lip.

"That's all well and good, but what is the purpose of being born only to be in a super debilitating or permanent vegetative state? I mean, that seems really cruel and pointless to me." She brought to mind the hundreds of people whom nurses get to know very well through the years, bedridden people with severe brain damage or other hellish infirmities that bring them back to us again and again with clogged feeding tubes, bedsores, and urinary infections that are almost impossible to avoid with continuous diaper use.

I thought about it before sharing one of Dr. Backman's anecdotes about this very thing. "Well, there might be something to that kind of existence," I began slowly, feeling around for the right words. Up to this point, I had totally agreed with her and recalled the hundreds of times I had thought this same thing as I turned patients from side to side to clean up bowel movement after bowel movement, day after day. I thought of my first job as a nursing assistant caring for people like the 38-year-old nursing home patient who had survived a devastating car accident only to remain in a permanent vegetative state. Sometimes her husband and child would visit, and I tried to imagine their odd in-between world of remaining in the life of their wife and mom, a person who was still here but not quite alive, at least not in a way that any of us would want to be. I still recall the day when I was bathing her and reported my concern about the blood under her bottom when I changed her sheets. The nursing supervisor, with her signature gruffness, explained that just because someone was comatose, it didn't mean she didn't menstruate.

I recounted the case Dr. Backman had described about her client who had wanted to uncover the purpose of her life with her son, a 10-year-old boy whose mental age was about 18 months. He wore diapers, had limited muscle tone, and required round-the-clock care. I was deeply moved by her discovery that, among other things, he had chosen this lifetime not only to discover things within himself, but to enrich the life-learning of all those around him, trusting them with great love to develop their gifts of compassion, patience, and strength in caring for him. He was an extremely advanced soul capable of a meaningful life far beyond our comprehension.

My cynical friend stirred her coffee thoughtfully before issuing a characteristically brief response. *If anyone could give a sound rebuttal, it would be her,* I thought as I watched her mulling this over. "Hmm. That's deep, missy." And with that, she changed the subject.

And so, because the concept of sacrificing oneself for the greater good sounds particularly old-school Christian to me, it puzzles me how and why it would be such a huge leap for modern-day religious folks to imagine that someone working with God's will might choose a seemingly brief or difficult life to learn about something incomprehensibly awful in order to help others on their journeys as well.

There was also an anecdote of a case where a client recalled being a very young child who had gotten swept away while playing at the beach. Before she was born, she had known this would happen, and she was calm knowing that her purpose in this brief go-round was to give her parents the gift of mind-blowing tragedy to turn their stable world upside down. Incredibly grim and maybe even cruel by human standards, but in the end, judging it as good or bad, right or wrong, useful or useless by human standards is very much beyond our grasp.

And so, without further ado, I bring you this last story that I have crafted for you, dear readers. The gist of it doesn't come from my own story, and I'm not able to give credit where credit is due because I cannot place where I read it. I only remember its powerful takeaway that touched me deeply so very long ago. Maybe it was in a magazine I leafed through in a doctor's office, maybe it was part of a novel or a bit in a newspaper. I think it might've been in a brochure I procured about being a good mom. At any rate, it made me pause and glimpse at unconventional possibilities as I grappled with my own angst stemming from the ephemeral brief puffs of life energy that passed through the abortion clinic, felt but not truly seen and certainly not acknowledged. I look forward to the day when the good people of the world can honor and thank all the energy around them without embarrassment, defensiveness, or disgrace.

TWENTY-EIGHT

Rochelle And Kelsey

"MAMA, ROLL THE WINDOW down! I want to get my face smacked by the wind!" Kelsey demanded as she smooshed her face against the cold pane of tempered glass that separated her from the swirling tempest of houses and trees whirring past her in a frenzied blur on the highway.

"All right, honey, I'll roll it down a little, but don't stick your face or fingers out too far. Stuff can come flying at you from nowhere way too fast and hurt you. And please remember to say *please* when you ask me for something." Rochelle pressed the button just enough to give her daughter about six inches of fresh air from the highway before glancing in the rearview mirror.

As is the case for millions of moms around the world, Rochelle never tired of stealing glimpses of her insanely perfect child whenever she got the chance. *How does this happen?* she thought. How is it that, time after time, Nature does its job so incredibly well, gifting most people with flawless babies born with two eyes, four limbs, and ten fingers and toes? And they're so pretty too! Kelsey ignored her mom as she stuck her pert little nose as far over as was permissible from her car seat and shoved her well-worn stuffed iguana's head through the crack so he could get a better whiff without falling out of the car. Rochelle marveled at the china doll face with the blond spirals bouncing happily around it and silently thanked God or whoever for the miracle of being this kid's mom.

Kelsey, having gotten her fill of face-smacking, settled back into her car seat and hummed a little tune before casually stating, "You know, Mama, I've been here before."

"Yes, honey, we've gone to Grampy's lots of times."

"Yeah, I know. I mean I've been *here* before."

"You mean in this car?" Rochelle asked with amusement at the very literal observations of a typical three-year-old who reels off in a nonstop stream of consciousness with authority and abandon. That and the endless "But why?" questions were a hallmark of this delightfully maddening developmental stage.

"No. Here!" Kelsey insisted again. Rochelle looked back to see Kelsey waggling her angelic head with much emphasis, nodding at nothing in particular.

"Oh. Um, no, I didn't know that," Rochelle absentmindedly responded as she switched lanes.

Comfortable stillness reigned for almost two whole minutes, and Rochelle figured that Kelsey had moved on to another subject. She flipped on the car stereo to the newest KIDZ BOP compilation and their safely sanitized version of a massively popular song that lamented horny sluts getting boned as it gently thumped out a rhythm into the silence. She was thankful yet again, this time for this watered-down version that gave parents much-needed alternatives in modern pop music so they could avoid hearing innocent filth spewing from their kids' sweet little mouths as they gleefully sang along to the seductively catchy tunes.

Kelsey began chattering seriously with her iguana, which she often did, every now and again stopping with a short pause to listen for his response before resuming. "Oh, you wanna know if I liked it here before? Oh yes, it was fun being in Mommy's tummy the last time too!"

Rochelle froze, hands gripping the steering wheel as she tried to get her bearings around this quirky conversation. Her heart skipped a beat as she lightly asked her daughter what she was talking about with Iggy the Iguana.

"Iggy wanted to know if I liked being here the last time, you know, when I was in your tummy."

Rochelle steadied herself and verified that she had indeed heard what she'd thought she'd heard. "You remember being in my belly before? Sweetheart, babies are way too little to be able to know what's happening. Remember how we talked about this?"

"Well, yes, but *I* remember it and lots of other stuff too, like when I lived on a farm with lots of brothers and sisters, and also the time Daddy and I fell off that boat into the freezing-cold water. I didn't like that at all!"

This was not the first time her daughter had talked about seeming past lives, and Rochelle reassured herself that, according to her pediatrician, this wasn't uncommon and she would grow out of it soon enough. She and her husband actually enjoyed listening to Kelsey's fantastic snippets of information about far-away places, pleased that they could foster their daughter's vivid imagination and sense of wonder. But this "recollection" hit way too close to home.

"Yes, I can imagine that must've been very scary," Rochelle replied using the language she had learned when reading an article about how to talk to a child when they describe past lives. *Listen just as you would with anything else they talk about, and emphasize that they are here and safe now*, the authors, physicians from the University of Virginia School of Medicine, advised.[55]

"Uh-huh, it was! But I liked the time when I was in your tummy. That was fun! And I liked coming back and finding you again!"

Rochelle squirmed uncomfortably in her seat. Could this little peanut be the one from before?

Kelsey continued. "I knew you were sad before, and you couldn't let me stay back then, so I liked it when I came back this time. You had funny curly hair then, but not now. I like your hair, Mommy," Kelsey said, straining forward as much as she could to barely graze Rochelle's silky, straight ponytail as it rested on the headrest just out of reach.

Rochelle felt her heart in her mouth as she focused intently on the highway. *Breathe, breathe, breathe.* She had pushed this memory out of her mind years ago, and here it was, back with a vengeance. Perms had been all the rage, and she had prided herself on being able to give herself a home perm like nobody's business. She had only recently grudgingly thrown out the rollers that had been stashed in the back of her bathroom cabinet once she realized that perms weren't going to make a comeback anytime soon. At age 17, she had been the hit of the roller rink with her chestnut ringlets and shapely legs as she whirled in the spotlight, usually solo but sometimes with a dance partner, his hands gripping her slim waist as he'd lift her overhead.

Those were her glory days, the time in her life when she knew she was not a rising star but had already arrived at the pinnacle of her achievements. She was content to know that it would all be over when she got to college, and, truthfully, she was okay with that. She watched the older skaters desperately grasping at straws to stay in the limelight and concluded that it was pathetic. She vowed to bow out gracefully and had already laid out other dreams and plans, before everything was put in jeopardy when she found out she was pregnant just two months before leaving for college.

The choice had been painful but not difficult. She absolutely wanted to pursue her dream of going away to a big university to partake in every aspect of college life. She had her abortion, cried, and moved on. It wasn't until years later, when she tried to get pregnant after enjoying several years of marriage, that her early loss hit her when, no matter what she and her husband did, she couldn't get pregnant. Only then did that easy, breezy conception hit her in the face with guilt. What if that had been her only shot at motherhood, and she had blown it? She knew that this was ridiculous and that her resentment at being a teen mom would not have allowed her to truly give all that she was now able to, but still, nagging doubt and shame nipped at her.

It had all been so secret. No one, not even her boyfriend, knew about her procedure. She drifted away from her friends and family for a while, carefully avoiding everyone until she felt herself return to normal. From her place in the world as the upstanding daughter of the associate pastor at a megachurch, there was just no way that this brief event could have any bearing on her life, and she upheld her role beautifully. When, to her relief, she finally got pregnant with Kelsey, she felt certain that God had answered her prayers and forgiven her for her early transgressions. That this precious cherub would bring up such a painful memory now jarred her to the core.

Realizing that it was her turn to say something, Rochelle weakly replied, "Why, thank you, honey. I love your hair too."

Moments later, they pulled into Grampy's nice neighborhood and then into his carefully sculpted driveway. Rochelle felt a huge wave of relief when she stepped out of her SUV and felt familiar ground beneath her feet. Kelsey bolted from her car seat and hurled herself happily into her beloved Grampy's waiting arms. This was their life in the present moment. Guilt and shameful secrets had no place on this fine October day, and even if they did rise to the surface, dreaded and unbidden, there was always the possibility that redemption could arise in the most unexpected of ways. Rochelle took a deep breath and steadied herself before gathering the overnight bags and heading for the door.

TWENTY-NINE

Justice And Leatherbacks

"Every single life is valuable in ways you cannot imagine (…) Every single life is a gift."

—Annie Kagan, from *The Afterlife of Billy Fingers*

WHEN MY KIDS WERE little, they hated it when I told them again and again that life's not fair. I usually strived to be cheerily matter-of-fact about this. I generally reserved this comment for times when it could be a lesson absorbed from what I considered a minor injustice, something that could easily be brushed off with a snuggle or a trip to the corner bakery. Unfortunately for me, my kids are very sensitive people, and even though they now grudgingly admit that there's never been a truer statement, they were invariably infuriated at me for trying to rob them of their lust for moral outrage at such a young age.

Moral outrage provides much necessary steam for getting a

lot of jobs done, but as I grow older, I just don't have too much of it left in me. Besides, I've been on too many different sides of any given fence to be fully convinced of the correctness of anything anymore. Therefore, in the haze of ambiguity, I leave my stories to you—truths located in my memories and the fictional tales I wrapped around them, partly from wanting to protect people and partly because I am truly awful at remembering specific details about any particular situation. I weave the genuineness of my stories through my imagination and hazy recall to give you a glimpse into the world as I've experienced it.

The unfairness of life rudely shoves me to the ground with surprising regularity, especially if I watch the news these days, which is expertly manufactured to get a rise out of even the meekest soul among us. While I grumble and sign petitions and wonder for the zillionth time why downtrodden people never seem to get a break, I need only look out my window or walk along the beach to see the cruelty of life walking hand in hand with its beauty.

I think of those adorable videos of baby sea turtles hatching on the beach and scurrying madly toward the water, usually with a few gorgeously muscled and tanned young volunteers doing their best to usher as many as they can toward safety. According to the National Ocean Service, only up to 1 in 10,000 will survive to adulthood.[41] Other than being a convenient source of nutrition for other animals, what's the point? And did these little fellas have the capacity to understand, when they signed up for this go-round on Planet Earth, that their life purpose would be to live for 32 seconds of glorious aliveness before getting eaten by a seagull? Does it make a difference to them if someone willfully chooses whether or not to annihilate or save them? What about the usefulness of the experience of the sentient being who snuffs them out or saves their life? If we're talking about the human species, then there's definitely something to *that*. Guilt or defensiveness are part and parcel of our existence, but what we do with our perceptions varies vastly from person to person and culture to culture. It's been entertaining, honestly, to see just how differently people prioritize what matters to them and why.

If you are a person who believes in the sanctity of human beings above all others, adhering to the belief that a human life is far more important than that of the chicken or shrimp you delightedly consume, I am honored and amazed that you have read this book in its entirety. Unlike the beautifully sensitive vegetarians I know, I eat my animal foods, but with reverence and keen awareness that—at this moment—I'm on *this* side in a food chain where there's a fine line between being the eater and the eaten. For the most part, I've made peace with life's injustices with a deep knowing that life is lived on many planes of existence, many far beyond the grasp of what most people would include in their definition of what it means to be alive. Life curls, twists, and turns all around us as we struggle and suffer and wail and delight in all that we have come for. To be able to sit with all of this is, for me, a reward of the very highest order after living with all my might.

I have recently found joy as an amateur mosaic artist. I have always loved seeing something that had been shattered into a million pieces come back together to form something so beautiful and so different than what it was originally. Even ugly things, like construction debris or the world's tackiest gravy boat, become striking accents as they weave their way through a new and complete structure. Of all the things that get shattered and rebuilt, the human spirit is by far my favorite.

Epilogue

TODAY IS NATIONAL ABORTION Provider Appreciation Day. I would surely not have known this if it weren't for the fact that after 20-some years, I find myself back in this arena working as a telemedicine nurse taking calls from patients who have questions or concerns after their abortion procedures. This was not my plan.

In completing this book, I decided that it would be a good idea to reconnect with some of the best of the best that I remembered from my days in the field to see what's changed since the turn of this century. I felt that I owed it to myself and my readers to give a clear picture of the current state of the art and how things have changed or stayed the same in this unique and, dare I say, underdiscussed sector of health care.

Just to give you some contrast, I pause here with a tiny smile at the memory of chatting with a friend who was diagnosed with breast cancer. I recall her genuine puzzlement over being treated like a rock star. It seems that some diagnoses are clearly more worthy of a pink emblem than others. Could you imagine professional athletes wearing insignia on their jerseys honoring courageous women whose primary medical diagnosis was unwanted pregnancy? But I digress. In asking for some stalwart abortion providers' feedback on my writing, a golden opportunity dropped into my lap after an old friend and colleague asked if I knew anyone who might want to take hotline calls. Having just lost my mercifully low stress end-of-career nursing job in an adult daycare due to the pandemic, I happily took the job myself.

This is what I've learned. The themes of the stories that you've just read are very much alive and well, but quite a few of the structures around the experiences have changed in many ways for the better, at least in the clinics that I've been dealing with. Despite the fact that newly imposed restrictions have already seen me talking to many impoverished women who are struggling with 12-hour road trips or expensive flights to obtain a simple abortion procedure, much progress has been made to normalize and humanize abortion care where it, thankfully, still exists at the moment. As with any forward-thinking groups, coalitions of abortion providers have banded together to come up with unique, family-centered care that is reflected in everything from lovely family waiting rooms complete with cozy cribs and toys to major cultural shifts in how staff communicate, with a zero-tolerance policy for sarcasm or cruelty.

Another major transformation that is underway is the paradigm shift of today's young women. While I still encounter a significant number of patients who cower in a closet to whisper their questions and concerns, I have an equal number who are more than comfortable discussing their issues within earshot of others. Not long ago, I marveled at a professional young woman calmly describing her vaginal blood clots to me while hailing and greeting an Uber driver on her way home from a business trip. Call it the "Age of Too Much Information," but I do have to admire the fearlessness that comes from growing up in a world where there is so little to be ashamed about. With a young professional daughter of my own, I have plenty of opportunities to see a common theme among today's women of childbearing age who confidently take control of their lives and who have little patience for outdated notions about the feminine mystique so lauded in days gone by. They see no reason for hiding themselves, their bodies, or their experiences.

I don't know what the future holds; as I write this, millions of Americans are either bracing themselves for a battle of epic legal proportions or are on their genuflected knees in the hope of having their prayers answered as we ready ourselves for the impending Supreme Court revisit of *Roe v. Wade*. What I do know is that there has never been a more critical time for personal and collectively courageous wisdom as we dig deep into our shared humanity on this precarious planet.

I am thankful grateful for this moment in time as I've taken this journey with you. I feel deep gratitude that I can share safely in this present moment, whatever that will look like for you as you read this.

Fondly, Patrice
March 10, 2022

Acknowledgments

"It took me a while, it took me the journey of this entire book, but I realized that there was a lesson, which was, in every scar there is a story. The salve is the telling itself."

—Emily Bernard, *Black is the Body*

UNFORGETTABLE PEOPLE (YOU KNOW who you are), LM, for her enthusiasm and unwavering expertise with a blue pencil; KL, JC, and ES for helping to make this the best possible version of my story; EB and CH for their keen insight; CO for her love, friendship, and stunning detail of her Argentinian heritage; SCC, OL, and LdJ for the fun conversations about finding the best Spanish slang terms for granny panties, from Spain to Puerto Rico and beyond; IC and PC for helping me sort out some multicultural points of view; my beautiful adult children for their honesty and patience; and DR, the anchor for my soul.

Endnotes

1   Riane Eisler, Sacred Pleasure: Sex, Myth, and the Politics of the Body
    (New York: HarperOne, 2011).

2   "mosaic," Lexico by Oxford English Dictionary, accessed April 8, 2022,
    https://www.lexico.com/en/definition/mosaic.

3   "mosaic novel," Oxford Reference, accessed April 8, 2022, https://www.
    oxfordreference.com/view/10.1093/acref/9780195305678.001.0001/
    acref-9780195305678-e-387.

4   Rebecca Wind, "Abortion Is a Common Experience for U.S. Women,
    Despite Dramatic Declines in Rates," Guttmacher Institute, October 19,
    2017, https://www.guttmacher.org/news-release/2017/abortion-common-
    experience-us-women-despite-dramatic-declines-rates.

5   Rachel K. Jones, Elizabeth Witwer, and Jenna Jerman, "Abortion
    Incidence and Service Availability in the United States, 2017,"
    Guttmacher Institute, September 2019, https://www.guttmacher.org/
    report/abortion-incidence-service-availability-us-2017.

6   Pam Belluck, "Abortion by Telemedicine: A Growing Options as Access
    to Clinic Wanes," the New York Times, updated June 29, 2020, https://
    www.nytimes.com/2020/04/28/health/telabortion-abortion-telemedicine.
    html.

7   Ushma D. Upadhyay, Chris Ahlbach, Shelly Kaller, Clara Cook, and
    Isabel Muñoz, "Trends In Self-Pay Charges And Insurance Acceptance
    For Abortion In The United States, 2017–20," Health Affairs 41,
    no. 4 (April 2022), https://www.healthaffairs.org/doi/10.1377/
    hlthaff.2021.01528.

8   Chavi Eve Karkowsky, "I Found the Outer Limits of my Pro-Choice
    Beliefs," The Atlantic, August 7, 2019, https://www.theatlantic.

com/ideas/archive/2019/08/pro-choice-ob-gyn-confronts-limits-her-beliefs/594151/.

9   "Rhesus (Rh) Factor: Incompatibility, Complications & Pregnancy," Cleveland Clinic, accessed November 18, 2021, https://my.clevelandclinic.org/health/diseases/21053-rh-factor.

10 "Abortion and Mental Health," American Psychological Association, updated June 2018, https://www.apa.org/topics/abortion.

11 "The Turnaway Study," University of California San Francisco, accessed April 8, 2022, https://www.ansirh.org/research/ongoing/turnaway-study.

12 "Abortion," American Psychological Association, updated June 2018, https://www.apa.org/topics/abortion.

13 Erin Blakemore, "The Criminalization of Abortion Began as a Business Tactic," History, May 25, 2019, https://www.history.com/news/the-criminalization-of-abortion-began-as-a-business-tactic.

14 "Abortifacients," ScienceDirect, accessed April 6, 2022, https://www.sciencedirect.com/topics/neuroscience/abortifacients.

15 Somia Gul, Bushra Rubab, Nameera Ahmed, Urooba Iqbal, Maduri Ranjeeth Kumar, and Lokanatha C Reddy, "Table 1: Various Abortifacient Herbs along with Their Relevant Part &..." ResearchGate, July 31, 2018, https://www.researchgate.net/figure/Various-abortifacient-herbs-along-with-their-relevant-part-preparations_tbl1_279446147.

16 Karen Abbott, "Madame Restell: The Abortionist of Fifth Avenue," Smithsonian magazine, November 27, 2012, https://www.smithsonianmag.com/history/madame-restell-the-abortionist-of-fifth-avenue-145109198/.

17 Ibid.

18 Ibid.

19 Anna M. Peterson, "From Commonplace to Controversial: The History of Abortion." Origins, November 2012, https://origins.osu.edu/article/commonplace-controversial-different-histories-abortion-europe-and-united-states.

20 Ibid.

21 Ibid.

22 "Anthony Comstock's 'Chastity' Laws," PBS, accessed April 8, 2022, https://www.pbs.org/wgbh/americanexperience/features/pill-anthony-comstocks-chastity-laws/.

23 Rachel Benson Gold, "Lessons from Before Roe: Will Past be Prologue?" Guttmacher Policy Review 6, no. 1 (March 1, 2003), https://www.guttmacher.org/gpr/2003/03/lessons-roe-will-past-be-prologue.

24 "Roe v. Wade," Britannica, accessed April 8, 2022, https://www.britannica.com/event/Roe-v-Wade.e

25 Joshua Collins, Daniela Díaz, "With Abortion Legalization, Colombia Joins South America's 'Green Wave'," World Politics Review, February 25, 2022, https://www.worldpoliticsreview.com/articles/30352/with-legalized-abortion-colombia-joins-south-america-s-green-wave.

26 "Irish Abortion Referendum: Ireland Overturns Abortion Ban," BBC News, May 26, 2018, https://www.bbc.com/news/world-europe-44256152.

27 "Progress Pays Off," Power to Decide, accessed April 8, 2022, https://powertodecide.org/sites/default/files/media/savings-fact-sheet-national.pdf.

28 Kate Bradford and Tahra Johnson, "State Policies on Sex Education in Schools," National Conference of State Legislatures (NCSL), October 1, 2020, https://www.ncsl.org/research/health/state-policies-on-sex-education-in-schools.aspx.

29 "High School YRBS," Centers for Disease Control and Prevention, accessed November 18, 2021, https://nccd.cdc.gov/youthonline/App/QuestionsOrLocations.aspx?CategoryId=C04.

30 "Sex and HIV Education," Guttmacher Institute, April 1, 2022, https://www.guttmacher.org/state-policy/explore/sex-and-hiv-education.

31 "gallows humor," Lexico by Oxford English Dictionary, accessed April 8, 2022, https://www.lexico.com/en/definition/gallows_humor.

32 Karima R. Sajadi-Ernazarova and Christopher L. Martinez, "Abortion Complications," StatPearls, updated May 24, 2021, https://www.ncbi.nlm.nih.gov/books/NBK430793/.

33 Ibid.

34 "Dilation and Curettage (D & C)," Cleveland Clinic, accessed May 16. 2022, https://my.clevelandclinic.org/health/treatments/4110-dilation-and-curettage-d--c.

35 "Pregnancy-Related Deaths," Centers for Disease Control, updated February 26, 2019, https://www.cdc.gov/reproductivehealth/maternalinfanthealth/pregnancy-relatedmortality.htm/.

36 Ushma D. Upadhyay, Sheila Desai, et al., "Incidence of Emergency Department Visits and Complications After Abortion," Obstetrics & Gynecology 125, no. 1 (January 2015): 175–183, https://www.doi.org/10.1097/AOG.0000000000000603.

37 "4 Common Pregnancy Complications," Johns Hopkins Medicine, accessed April 6, 2022, https://www.hopkinsmedicine.org/health/conditions-and-diseases/staying-healthy-during-pregnancy/4-common-pregnancy-complications.

38 Elizabeth G Raymond and David A Grimes, "The comparative safety of legal induced abortion and childbirth in the United States," Obstetrics and gynecology, 119 no. 2 part 1 (February 2012), https://pubmed.ncbi.nlm.nih.gov/22270271/.

39 Dave Levitan, "Unspinning the Planned Parenthood Video," FactCheck.org, July 24, 2015, https://www.factcheck.org/2015/07/unspinning-the-planned-parenthood-video/.

40 Emma Green, "Why Indiana, and Other States, Are Requiring Aborted Fetuses to Be Buried or Cremated," The Atlantic, May 14, 2016, https://www.theatlantic.com/politics/archive/2016/05/state-mandated-mourning-for-aborted-fetuses/482688/.

41 "Fetal Remains," British Pregnancy Advisory Service, 2015, https://www.bpas.org/more-services-information/fetal-anomaly-care/fetal-remains/.

42 Rachel Kurzius, "One Woman's Expensive Trek from Georgia to Maryland to Get an Abortion Is Not at All Uncommon," DCist, October 28, 2018, https://dcist.com/story/17/08/10/georgia-student-maryland-abortion/.

43 Chris Bodenner, "Personal Stories of Abortion Made Public," The Atlantic, February 27, 2017, https://www.theatlantic.com/notes/all/2016/01/personal-stories-of-abortion-made-public/423831/.

44 "Domestic Abuse Against Pregnant Women," Best Beginnings, accessed April 6, 2022, https://www.bestbeginnings.org.uk/domestic-abuse.

45 "Unitarian Universalism's Seven Principles," UUA.org, July 20, 2017, https://www.uua.org/beliefs/what-we-believe/principles.

46 Roy J. Levin, "Wet and Dry Sex—the Impact of Cultural Influence in Modifying Vaginal Function," Sexual and Relationship Therapy 20, no. 4 (2005): 465–74, https://doi.org/10.1080/14681990500396568.

47 Colin Tidy, "Gravidity and Parity Definitions (Implications in Risk Assessment)," Patient.info, January 21, 2019, https://patient.info/doctor/gravidity-and-parity-definitions-and-their-implications-in-risk-assessment.

48 "History of IAFN-International Association of Forensic Nurses," International Association of Forensic Nurses, 2014, https://www.forensicnurses.org/page/AboutUS.

49 Sara Newmann, Andrea Dalve-Endres, Justin Diedrich, Eleanor Drey, Karen Meckstroth, and Jody E Steinauer, "Cervical Preparation for Second Trimester Surgical Abortion," Cochrane Database of Systematic Reviews, July 16, 2008, https://doi.org/10.1002/14651858.cd007310.

50 "Human Trafficking by the Numbers," Human Rights First, January 7, 2017, https://www.humanrightsfirst.org/resource/human-trafficking-numbers.

51 Christopher Ingraham, "The Percentage of American Adults Not Having Sex Has Reached a Record High," ScienceAlert, April 1, 2019, https://www.sciencealert.com/the-percentage-of-americans-not-having-sex-has-reached-a-record-high.

52 Frank Newport, "Americans, Including Catholics, Say Birth Control Is Morally OK," Gallup, May 22, 2012, https://news.gallup.com/poll/154799/americans-including-catholics-say-birth-control-morally.aspx.

53 "Contraceptive Use in the United States by Demographics," Guttmacher Institute, May 28, 2021, https://www.guttmacher.org/fact-sheet/contraceptive-use-united-states.

54 Linda Backman, Bringing Your Soul to Light: Healing through Past Lives and the Time Between (Woodbury, MN: Llewellyn Publications, 2009).

55 "Advice to Parents of Children who are Spontaneously Recalling Past Life Memories, University of Virginia School of Medicine, Division of Perceptual Studies, accessed April 18, 2022, https://med.virginia.edu/ perceptual-studies/resources/advice-to-parents-of-children-who-are-spontaneously-recalling-past-life-memories/.

Printed in Great Britain
by Amazon